DAN TYLER MOORE

wolves,widows, and orphans

THE WORLD PUBLISHING COMPANY
Cleveland and New York

Published by The World Publishing Company
2231 West 110th Street, Cleveland, Ohio 44102

Published simultaneously in Canada by
Nelson, Foster & Scott, Ltd.

First Printing 1967

Library of Congress Catalog Card Number 66–25886

PRINTED IN THE UNITED STATES OF AMERICA

To Betty
without whose help
this book
would never have been written

WOLVES, WIDOWS, AND ORPHANS

FOREWORD

♠

Confidence men exist and even prosper for a time because there is a tinge of larceny in even the most righteous of their fellow men. It is a rare individual who will shy away from a chance to make a quick buck or avoid an opportunity to get something for nothing. This is what the late, great W. C. Fields meant when he said, "You can't cheat an honest man."

Many of Dan Tyler Moore's stories in the pages that follow show the extent to which the "suckers" and "marks" often go in their quests to be "taken."

For the wise, these stories make entertaining reading. For the gullible and unwary, they sound an amusing alert.

CONTENTS

♠

WOLVES, WIDOWS, AND ORPHANS

♠

THE ULTRA-POWER PILL

Many years ago the startled officials of the General Electric Company's main office in Schenectady, New York, received a mysterious letter:

> Gentlemen:
> After many years of research, I have finally succeeded in developing a power pill which concentrates the power contained in a full bucket of gasoline into a capsule not much bigger than an aspirin tablet. I intend to submit this pill to you for testing on Thursday of next week, so that your research laboratory can quickly ascertain the value of this invention by actual scientific tests.
> I am prepared, of course, for the reaction on your part that this is a crank letter that should be completely ignored. It is my suggestion that you first send an unimportant official, one whose time is not too valuable, to my hotel to watch my demonstration. I can assure you that his report will result in your immediately sending someone of real capacity to confirm his report.

Although I have a strong aversion to being cast
as a melodramatic person, my invention is so funda-
mental in concept, and will have such serious reper-
cussions on the operation of important corporations
now exploiting energy sources such as coal and oil,
that I would fear for my life if the facts concerning
my secret became generally known.

Lest my fears appear overly dramatic, I respectfully call your attention to the case of Rudolf Diesel,
who, after inventing the diesel engine, which enormously decreased the world's expenditure for liquid
fuels, was thrown overboard from his liner in the
middle of the Atlantic. It is generally accepted that
this act was perpetrated by agents of the large oil
combines.

I will telephone your President's office next
Thursday morning from the hotel to ascertain what
steps have been taken to monitor my demonstration.

Very truly yours,

/s/ Gaston Bulmar

The hilarious top echelon of the General Electric
Company decided that this was their letter of the week. It
was good, certainly, as a top conversation piece at dinner
parties, so with tongue in cheek, they decided to play it
straight.

On Mr. Bulmar's arrival in Schenectady an assistant
to the Third Vice-President, a bright, young, bushy-tailed
graduate of the Harvard Business School named Forest
Golland, was sent over to his hotel. He found Mr. Bulmar,
the pill's inventor, in an advanced case of jitters. He was a
tall, blue-eyed, intelligent-looking man, very conservatively dressed, with the tiny red ribbon of the French
Legion of Honor stitched across his lapel.

Mr. Bulmar looked at his visitor wryly. "I feel like an absolute damn fool," he said, "acting in such a cops and robbers capacity. It may well be my overwrought imagination, but every time I pass someone in the hall of the hotel, I can't help feeling he knows what I am here for."

Bulmar smiled an engaging smile. "I know this is probably all tommyrot, but I also know that if any of the major oil interests ever found out about this pill, my life wouldn't be worth ten cents."

The young General Electric official gave the inventor the sort of smile a mother gives an infant. "You don't have to worry about anything like that," he said. "We haven't told anybody, and we are not going to. General Electric, after all, isn't a corner grocery store. We have some power too, and we will see that you are protected. Now tell me, what's the deal?"

The keen blue eyes of the inventor softened as he pointed to the top of the dresser. "See those ten pills?"

The young G.E. executive stared. They looked like ten aspirin tablets arranged in a row on the dresser.

"My first job, of course, is to persuade you people I am not just a crackpot, or someone trying to pull a phony deal. Let's get that part of my job out of the way right now. I want you to choose any one of those pills and toss it into this bucket." Mr. Bulmar held up an ordinary wash bucket with a wire handle.

The young man took one of the middle pills and tossed it into the bucket. It landed with a loud clink. The inventor opened the door of the bathroom. "Now watch this," he said. He turned on the cold-water faucet of the bathtub and let the water run into the bucket. The pill dissolved almost instantly with a hissing sound and a cloud of white bubbles. A second later there was a strong smell of gasoline in the air.

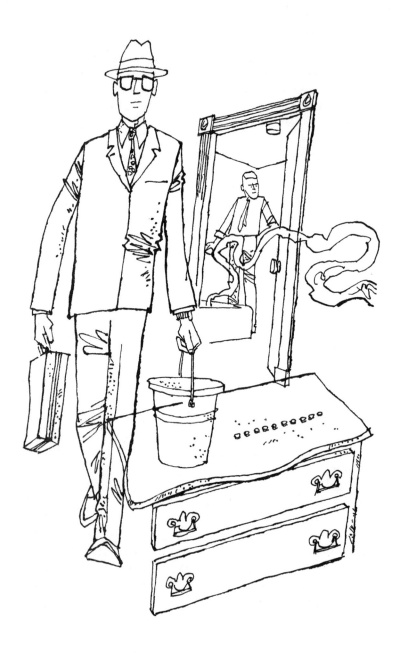

The inventor looked up smiling. "Smell that? I've got a cover here for the bucket so you won't spill it. I want you to take the whole works back to your General Electric testing laboratory and have them test it." Again Bulmar flashed his brilliant smile. "And I'll tell you exactly what they are going to find—just plain ordinary gasoline. Or something so close to it that they won't be able to tell the difference. Try it in an automobile, analyze it, try it in a gasoline lamp. It will pass all of their most searching tests as a high grade fuel! Wild horses couldn't get me out of this room; I will be sitting right here waiting for your call."

The goggled-eyed young G.E. executive took the bucket back to the testing laboratory, where its content was indeed found to be top quality gasoline. His excited report was greeted by his superior with tolerant skepticism. "It's just some sort of trick. There just has to be a trick somewhere."

The next day G.E. sent over a top-level member of its legal department to see what it was all about. The inventor repeated the experiment and, while he was putting the rubber cover over the bucket, the deeply impressed General Electric official asked him exactly what his deal was. What did he want?

The blue eyes of the inventor hardened. "The two things that are most important to me," he said, "are: one, to get paid for what may well be the greatest invention of all time; two, to try my best not to get myself killed by the oil companies."

Mr. Bulmar's lips turned down in a grim hard line. "Unfortunately, my two objectives are directly opposed to one another. If I didn't mind being killed it would be easy to get this thing patented, auction it off to the highest bidder, and get a gigantic price for it. If, on the other hand, I didn't care about the money, I could throw my formulas into the trash basket and be in no danger of my life. The big trouble is that I want both. That's why I came to you people, and that's why I have kept this thing so completely under wraps. I want both, so I am going to have to make a compromise both with my safety and with the money I am going to get."

The inventor paused. "The reason I have asked your people from G.E. in each case to pick one out of the ten pills on the dresser is because I wanted you to be sure they are all exactly the same—and they are. What I want is to sell the remaining pills on the dresser to the General Electric Company for one hundred thousand dollars. When your research department analyzes them, your scientists will immediately see how I have done what I have done. They will immediately kick themselves all over the lot for not thinking of it themselves. To help you further, I am going to give you a memorandum which will make everything quicker and easier. This won't be absolutely necessary but it will save you most of the work of analysis."

Again the cold blue eyes hardened. "One thing I want to avoid, at all costs, is any chance of getting into a legal tangle which would expose to the world what I have invented before I actually get my money and get myself to a safe place. I am not the least bit interested in this proposition unless I can put the pills and the formula, right in front of your representatives, into a safety box in the local bank. I will then give you a paper saying that the General Electric Company is authorized to open the safety deposit box and keep its contents *after one week*. I need one week to disappear with my hundred thousand dollars. I assure you I am going to disappear so completely that no one on earth will ever be able to find me. Not even you. I don't intend to become another Rudolf Diesel."

The lawyer was incredulous. "You are certainly asking for a blank check."

"And with good reason. You can send anyone else

you want into this hotel room to confirm the virtue of
these pills."

"Yes, but what if we open the safety deposit box and
there is nothing on the paper that is supposed to have the
formula?"

"You'll still have the pills. I will put them into the
safety deposit vault right before your representative's eyes.
Even if there was nothing on the piece of paper, that
wouldn't make any difference. Once your research department has the pills you will soon have my secret. Anyway,"
the man said, "that's one small risk you are going to have
to take if you want the pills. After all, G.E. isn't risking its
life and I am! If I didn't care about my life, you can be
sure the price would be a lot more than a hundred thousand dollars."

Mr. Bulmar stood up. "If the General Electric Company is not willing to do as I ask, there is absolutely no
need for us to discuss this matter further. It may well be
that Westinghouse or one of the other companies with
large research departments would be safer for me anyway."

Upon the lawyer's return to the General Electric
office, he electrified the top echelon by recommending that
the offer be immediately accepted. "After all," he said, "the
inventor's pill seems to work, and any chemical analysis is
certainly going to show us something extraordinary. Anything that can compress hundreds of millions of foot-
pounds of energy into something the size of an aspirin pill
just has to be on the unusual side. There obviously must
be some new chemical or physical laws involved and,
after all, that's the business we are in. New Ideas. I think
we would be crazy not to risk a hundred thousand on a
look-see this interesting."

"I think I am going to go over and take a look
myself."

Everyone turned around and looked at the speaker. It

was Irving Langmuir, the famous head of the General Electric Research Department. He was the first Nobel Prize winner the United States ever produced, the discoverer of the lattice atom, and one of the greatest scientific minds in the world.

Langmuir went to the hotel, listened to the inventor's proposition, chose a pill from the dresser, and watched him convert the bath water into gasoline.

Langmuir sat down on the inventor's bed with his head in his hands, thinking. If this were a fraud, he wondered, how could such a trick possibly be done? He looked at Mr. Bulmar. If *he* were this man and *he* were trying to defraud the General Electric Company, how, exactly, would he do it? As he sat thinking, the inventor watched him with a tolerant smile.

Finally Langmuir got to his feet. He went into the bathroom and turned on the faucet. Immediately a smell of gasoline permeated the room. He stared at the "inventor." Raw gasoline was coming out of the faucet. As he suspected, Mr. Bulmar had brought his own gasoline into the hotel with him and had pumped it into the bathtub faucet against the pressure of the city water by use of a portable electric pump. When he drew water out of the faucet, it flowed gasoline and there was no need for the pill to do anything but dissolve to complete the fraud.

By the time the General Electric Company had notified the Schenectady Police Department, one of the most extraordinary confidence men in American history had completely vanished.

The brilliance of Irving Langmuir saved the General Electric Company, but it is rumored that another large and famous U.S. corporation paid out the $100,000 and has been keeping top secret for many years the fact that it was defrauded.

OUT WITH THE LIGHTS

♠

At the turn of the century a group of well-dressed, aristo-cratic-looking conspirators were working together in a darkened home in the tiny kingdom of Monaco on the French coast.

They were the members of the famous "Black Gang," a group that specialized in violent, daring holdups of banks, post offices, and other places where there was cash in abundance to be picked up.

Black George, the gang's leader, a huge tiger of a man whose pale blue eyes looked incongruous beneath his coal-black hair, glowered at his companions. "The main thing," he said, "is to find where a great big pot of money is and then go after it by brute force." He paused. "We have brute force enough to go after almost anything, so our only question is, 'What exactly do we go after that gets us the most money per unit of brute force?'"

His companions looked at him blankly. Black George was always asking impossible rhetorical questions and then answering them himself. They settled back. What they did and how they did it had become strictly his

11

problem, and no one knew it better than Black George himself. As soon as he had played through his little game with all the silly questions, he would tell them what was next on the program and they would rake it in, the way they always did.

Black George lowered his voice dramatically. "There is only one place in the world," he said, "where fortunes of gold and silver and paper money are spread out on tables like canapés all ready to be eaten." He held up his hand. "And where the public is not denied access to them but is actually invited and encouraged to stand around the tables within easy reaching distance."

Black George smiled. The blank looks were all gone, there was no doubt about that. "It's the Monte Carlo Casino," he said triumphantly.

There were grumbles of dissent around the room. "It's the most heavily guarded building in Europe," a voice cried out. "Everyone knows they have guards with rifles standing behind loopholes, two floors up, overlooking the gambling tables."

Black George nodded patiently. "And so they have, and that is exactly how we will take them, by taking advantage of their own inflexible organization. They have no guards on the playing floor, only roulette croupiers and attendants. There are ten high-limit tables. At each of these, lying on the table between the croupier and the players, there will be over a million francs!"

Black George paused for effect. "My idea is to have three of our men playing at each table. Each one will have his gun and a light silk bag. One will stand next to the croupier and the other two will edge over near those players that have the most money in front of them. When the action is at its height, which is usually about ten o'clock, all the lights in the Casino will suddenly go out. The guards, crouched behind their loopholes two floors up, will not be able to see a thing. Instantly all thirty of our men will draw their guns and shoot the two players next to them, and, of course, the croupier. They will then all shout 'Run for your lives!' at the top of their voices. What with the yelling and the gunshots and the screams of those who have been shot in the darkness, everyone in the Casino will stampede madly out of the building, leaving his money on the table."

Black George paused to let the scene sink in. "And then our men will fill up their silk bags with at least ten million francs, which is at least half a million English pounds, or two million American dollars," he smiled, "depending upon when and where we want to spend it. Our horses will be standing outside. Before the Casino guards can leave their useless loopholes and stumble down two floors in the darkness, we will have galloped over the French border, only a few hundred yards away, and be perfectly safe in another jurisdiction."

Black George looked impatiently from one face to another. There was certainly an impressed silence in the room, but wasn't anyone going to ask the obvious question?

"Who will turn out the lights? Why will all the lights suddenly go out?"

Black George beamed. "I will," he said, holding up an enormous pair of rubber-handled cable cutters. "I have located the main electric cable going into the Casino. Insulated by rubber shoes and rubber gloves, I will cut it at exactly ten o'clock tonight. Your silk bags are over there on the table and you all have your guns. We will rendezvous at ten thirty on the main road two miles beyond the border."

Later that night the members of the Black Gang were all positioned around the ten high-limit tables. It was nine thirty and Black George was crouching in the power shed behind the Casino. The huge copper bus bars gleamed in the flickering light of his lantern. He stared at his watch.

As the minute hand approached ten o'clock he put the steel blades of the cable cutter against the copper.

At exactly ten o'clock Black George squeezed the long handles of the cable cutter together. There was a blinding electric flash that made him close his eyes spasmodically. He felt a violent tingling in his arms, and a brilliant flaming arc curved and sputtered between the cut pieces of copper. The lights that illuminated the outside of the Casino dimmed and flickered.

Black George, despite the ominous electric tingling in his hands, grasped one end of the severed copper in the jaws of the cable cutter and pulled violently. The flaming arc widened and extinguished, and suddenly he was in darkness.

He hurried out of the door of the power shed. All the lights outside of the Casino were out. . . . Inside the Casino, to the astonishment of his tensely waiting confederates, the lights flickered and dimmed down only to about half strength. The baffled members of the Black Gang, realizing that something was wrong and fearing that their plot had been uncovered, turned and, to the amazement of the players around the tables, ran pell-mell out of the Casino. To the vast puzzlement of the bystanders, they jumped on their horses and galloped wildly off into the night.

It turned out that the crafty Monsieur Blanc, the proprietor of the Casino, suspecting that some day this trick might be pulled, had, unbeknownst to the public, installed two sets of subsidiary lights inside the electric chandeliers. The chandeliers were lit not only by electricity but by gas and kersosene as well.

It turned out to be a startlingly good investment. Monsieur Blanc's later substitution of elaborately illuminated chips for cash further increased the security of the Casino.

THE GREAT ROULETTE SQUEEZE

♠

Monsieur Blanc, the proprietor of the Monte Carlo Casino in its salad days, was a very methodical and scientific-minded person. The winnings of his Casino were so mathematically consistent that he could estimate each day's earnings almost exactly by merely counting the number of people admitted to the gaming rooms.

One day, to his horror, Monsieur Blanc found that the money taken in was $40,000 less than it should have been, considering the admission figures. Investigation showed the total loss appeared to be focused on one roulette wheel. The croupier of that wheel, one of the most trusted and experienced in the Casino, remembered that the heaviest winner was playing an unorthodox and complicated doubling system that alternated between rouge and noir. He seemed to play both black and red about the same number of times, so his winnings evidently had nothing to do with the wheel.

Monsieur Blanc was intrigued. Although it was very unusual for the Casino average to be out that much after a day's play, by the law of averages it had to happen occasionally. He left orders that if the successful player came back he wanted to be called to watch him. Although the mathematicians always assured him that it was impossible to develop a roulette system that could beat the Casino, one could never be too careful.

The next night Monsieur Blanc was standing at the same table when the croupier gave him the agreed signal. The winner of the night before was back.

Almost immediately, to Monsieur Blanc's surprise, the man started winning again. Monsieur Blanc watched him carefully. The man would start by making a reasonably heavy bet on black. If he won, his winnings went into a special pile and he left the original bet where it was. If he lost, though, he would double his bet and put it on red instead of black. If he won, then of course he got his lost money back—plus the sum of his original bet. He put this sum in his winnings pile and returned to his original bet, which he put on black. If, after doubling, he lost a second time, he doubled still again, making the bet four times as large. Monsieur Blanc smiled compassionately. His smile had a touch of regret in it. It was only the old familiar doubling system after all. The poor fellow would eventually come to a point where a run of losses would bring his doubling bet up to the Casino's upper-betting limit and he would lose everything.

There was only one trouble with that theory. *The man won over a quarter of a million dollars and broke the bank.*

Monsieur Blanc was incredulous. Not once had the lucky man been forced to keep doubling until he reached the betting limit. He had always won before that happened.

Monsieur Blanc was worried. There were, he decided, only four possible explanations. The man could be incredibly lucky, the Casino could have a crooked croupier, the roulette wheel could be crooked, or—Monsieur

Blanc shuddered slightly—the man could have found a successful roulette system.

Monsieur Blanc stood watching the man play. It wasn't luck. He was sure of that. Every other player who had broken the bank had been a plunger, one who made enormous bets and won a succession of them. It didn't take many of them to break the bank. This player was different. He was slowly but surely winning hundreds of bets. The zero on the wheel should have eaten him up long ago, but for some reason it hadn't.

Monsieur Blanc looked at the croupier. No chance of crookery there. Anyhow, there had been a different croupier yesterday.

Monsieur Blanc wiped the perspiration from his forehead. It couldn't be a crooked wheel, because the player was mixing his bets all over the table, and on both black and red. A crooked wheel that enabled a man to win with bets *that* mixed up would have to be controlled by the croupier. Two crooked croupiers in a row? Absolutely impossible. Also, with guards patrolling the grounds of the Casino day and night, how could anyone ever get at one of their roulette wheels to fix it?

The perspiration was pouring off his face as Monsieur Blanc realized that the nightmare had finally come true. It must be a successful roulette system, the nightmare that all of the mathematicians swore to heaven was impossible.

Monsieur Blanc started scribbling the man's bets on a pad. He simply had to get some facts and figures for his mathematicians. It might well be the end of the Casino world as they knew it. For half an hour he jotted down all of the man's bets. Suddenly his mouth fell wide open. The man's first bets were always on black. When he lost, though, he shifted to red and kept doubling until he won. Blanc turned around and started for his office. It was a system all right. "Change the wheel at table five," he

ordered, "and have someone follow the winner until we identify him." Monsieur Blanc added, "He will leave as soon as the wheel is changed."

The man left as Monsieur Blanc predicted and the whole story eventually came out. The wheel was found to be faulty. The flanges had been squeezed together very slightly in such a way that it was harder for the ivory ball to fall into a black space than a red one.

The player knew that if he played nothing but red, and won, they would have immediately changed the wheel. His system was only to keep the management from thinking its wheel was crooked.

The most extraordinary part of the plot, however, was the method used to squeeze the wheel. The mysterious winner had originally come in with his "six-year-old son" who was, in reality, a circus midget dressed up as a young boy. Unbeknownst to the dense crowd at the table, the "boy" had slipped beneath the curtain that hung down to the floor around the table. He had remained under the table until the Casino had closed for the night. As soon as everyone left, the midget came out with a pair of pliers and squeezed together the black spaces on the wheel. They were squeezed together ever so slightly, but it was enough to cost the Casino close to a third of a million dollars.

Monsieur Blanc immediately did two things. First, he put all of the roulette wheels and other gambling devices on solid marble blocks so no one could get under them again. Secondly, he had a count made of the number of people who left the Casino, as well as of those who came in. If there was a discrepancy, the Casino was not closed until the missing person was located.

THE FORMIDABLE OLD LADY

♠

A rich, suspicious old lady, whom we will call Mrs. Russel MacAndrews, lived in a huge Columbus, Ohio, mansion with a houseful of servants who catered to her every whim. Her neighbors said she was so suspicious and stingy that she even distrusted banks and safety deposit vaults. She made no bones about the fact that she kept all her money and securities hidden in caches and wall safes around the house.

Such rumors of wealth carelessly stored posed an attractive challenge to the underworld, and from time to time burglars, sneak thieves, and even major top-echelon gangsters "cased the joint" with larceny in mind. Such gentry were always discouraged by four dismaying facts:

1. There were neat metal plaques on all the doors which said, "House protected by burglar alarm with independent electrical source."

2. The old lady's Japanese butler, Yojimbo, who worshipped her almost as a goddess, was always giving the awestruck neighborhood boys impromptu jiujitsu

lessons. He was also known to be a crack shot with a pistol, which was always on his person.

3. The old lady, a great sportswoman, had two enormous Chorban Copeks, Steppes wolf-killing dogs, Attila and Yavuz, which she had imported from Turkey and which had the free run of the house and yard. There was a disturbingly persistent story around the neighborhood that one burglar, evidently a man with more courage than brains, had somehow entered the house without setting off the burglar alarm. The two blue-eyed monsters killed him so swiftly and silently that only one anguished scream was heard by the electrified neighbors. All that was left the next morning was a spot of blood on the red Kazakh rug in the lady's living room. The butler, it was reported, tidied it up and it was said to have actually improved the subtlety of the rug's design.

4. The old lady, despite her age, was still, after thirty years, the Skeet Champion of the Columbus Gun and Dog Club.

The problem of evading the burglar alarm, surviving Attila and Yavuz and Yojimbo, only to run into the formidable old lady waiting patiently at the top of the stairs with her twelve-gauge shotgun loaded with number nine shot, was too much for the "Fancy." The underworld left Mrs. MacAndrews strictly alone.

One afternoon, as Mrs. MacAndrews was sitting in the bay window of her house looking out at the activity on the street, a company car drew up under the porte-cochere. She peered through the window at the inscription on the side of the car—"General Motors Stock Transfer Agent." The old lady looked smug. It was nice being the owner of five thousand shares of General Motors stock. Those dividends certainly helped keep the wolf from the door. She smiled to herself. Not that he had ever got within a mile of it.

The stock transfer agent, like many lower-echelon company officials, was extremely correct and formal. "I would like to see Mrs. Russel MacAndrews," he said.

"I am Mrs. MacAndrews," she replied. "You must have some good news for me."

The stock transfer agent smiled thinly, but his face lost none of its formality. "Some people would think it was good news," he said. He took a leather folder out of his pocket and handed it to her. It had his picture on it and identified him as Mr. George Evans, the General Motors Stock Transfer Agent for the Greater Columbus, Ohio, area.

"Am I right, Mrs. MacAndrews, in understanding that you are the owner of five thousand shares of our company's stock?"

"Your information is correct," she said.

"You will be interested, then, to read in tomorrow morning's paper that our Board of Directors has declared a stock dividend and is splitting the corporation's common shares two for one."

The old lady's smug expression vanished. She clasped her hands together in delight. "That means I'll have twice as much money, doesn't it?" she asked.

The stock transfer agent looked at her regretfully. "Unfortunately not, Mrs. MacAndrews," he said, "although many people make that very natural mistake. You see, the corporation is still exactly the same corporation. The only difference is that it now has twice as many shares. Each share will be worth half as much, but you will have twice as many of them." Again he smiled his frosty smile. "The funny thing is, though, Mrs. MacAndrews, that you probably will be making a considerable amount of money, despite the fact that the company's assets have not changed one bit. For some strange reason, when a corporation splits its stock two for one, the two shares are almost always worth more than the one they replaced. Don't ask me why. Maybe it goes up because people think the shares will go up. Whenever enough people think a stock is going up it usually does—even if the rise is unjustified."

The stock transfer agent opened his attaché case and took out her new stock certificate. "Anyway," he said, "you get ten thousand shares where you only had five thousand before. Here is the certificate. I will have to have your shares properly endorsed, so that they can be officially cancelled."

The old lady went up to her wall safe, brought down her certificates, endorsed them to bearer, and took delivery of her ten thousand shares.

The stock transfer agent's mouth opened with astonishment. "Am I to understand that you keep five thousand shares of our company's stock unguarded in your own home? That's an extremely dangerous and unusual thing to do. They should be locked up in a safety deposit box."

The old lady smiled. "Don't be too sure they are not guarded better than that," she said.

The stock transfer agent stood up. His face reflected his disapproval. "Is there anything else I can do for you, Mrs. MacAndrews?" he asked.

"Not a thing," she said happily. "Just make my shares go up as much as possible, whether it makes any sense or not."

The next General Motors dividend date was a rich experience for the old lady—because no dividends came in at all on her ten thousand shares.

She wrote an indignant letter to the company and checked with her broker and found to her horror that she was no longer listed as a stockholder. She had carelessly signed her shares over to a "one-hundred-per-center" who was posing as the General Motors Stock Transfer Agent. The certificate for ten thousand shares that he had given her was a crude counterfeit.

This type of confidence man is called a hundred-per-center because his share of the deal is exactly one hundred per cent. The phony stock transfer agent had the whole period from the day of the phony transfer until the next dividend date to sell the stock she had signed over to him, cover up his tracks, and make a clean getaway.

This nonviolent aristocrat of the crime world had adapted easily to conditions that scared the daylights out of the violent members of the "smash, bang, and shoot" fraternity.

THE CARDS IN THE SUN

♠

One of the greatest gambling cities in all history was Cairo, Egypt, during and after World War II. Unlike the gambling in Europe, which was largely in casinos, most of the gambling in Egypt was in private clubs and homes. King Farouk and other members of the Royal Family, and the small class of pashas who owned the country, were so wealthy that money meant almost nothing. In clubs like the Mohammed Ali Club and the Gezira Club the betting was probably higher than any other place on earth. The postwar boom was on. Hundreds of millions of dollars were still floating around from the Allied occupation and, next to women, gambling was the principal occupation of the Egyptian male upper class.

One day an attractive and titled Englishman, whom we will refer to as "Sir James," went to Cairo on a visit and began making the rounds of the embassies. The scion of a well-known British family, he was properly presented and lionized by the right people. The pashas found to their delight that Sir James, obviously a man of great wealth, loved to gamble as much as they did and that, although he seemed to lose a lot more than he won, he lost with such gentlemanly grace that he quickly became one of the most accepted and sought after men about town.

One of Sir James' favorite games, although it took him a while to get used to it, was the Middle Eastern version of American poker, in which all the cards under seven were taken out of the deck. This, of course, upset all the odds and mixed up the values so much that it even changed the sequence of winning hands. A flush, for example, was higher than a full house in Cairo poker. Whereas most of the American and English players avoided the game for this reason, Sir James paid the pashas the great compliment of observing that he liked their game better than regular poker. Another thing the pashas liked about Sir James was that he was always willing to take on the nuisance job of being the banker.

One day Sir James won a considerable amount of money at the Mohammed Ali Club from a Turk named Osman Bey. He had played with the Turk on numerous occasions and for some time had had a queer, uneasy feeling about him. On this particular night his feelings turned out to be exactly right. Osman Bey suggested that they have a drink after the game and Sir James, being such a substantial winner, could hardly refuse. They each ordered an Uzo and water and sat watching the smoky clouds appear in the liquid when the water was poured in.

Osman Bey sipped his drink and then stared with disconcerting directness across the table. "Sir James," he said, "this is not a friendly drink. This is a business conference. For some weeks now I have played cards with you. It has taken a little doing but I have clearly established that you are a card cheat. . . ."

Sir James started to rise to his feet.

Osman Bey looked at him arrogantly. "Sit down," he snapped, "and don't make a damned fool of yourself. You know you are a card cheat just as well as I do, and if you do anything embarrassing or foolish, I'm going to start yelling it out right here to everyone in the club."

Sir James sank back into his chair. "I don't understand," he stammered.

Osman Bey looked at him impatiently. "The quicker we get over this ridiculous sparring-around stage, the quicker we are going to find out whether I expose you right now or make a deal with you that will enable you to continue cheating."

Osman Bey looked at Sir James amiably. "Now that's a little better." He sipped his Uzo. "I first suspected you were a cheat when you were banking a poker game here at the club and complained bitterly about being a big loser. Although the bookkeeping was pretty complicated, what with everyone buying in and out, it looked to me as if you were really a big winner and were trying to conceal it for some reason. The next time you banked a game, I counted the money in and out as people bought and cashed in their chips. You won over ten thousand dollars in that game and claimed you lost over a thousand. I took the deck of cards home after the game but couldn't find any marks on them. I was puzzled because I saw the club steward bring the cards in and saw that the government seal on the cards was still intact. You certainly had no chance to mark them and they didn't seem to be marked."

Osman Bey laughed. "I kept testing you and experimenting and found that you won heavily only when you played with cards that had bicycle designs on the back. When I introduced a different type of pack into the game you did no better than anyone else. Of course, most of the cards sold in Cairo *are* bicycle cards so you won practically every game."

Sir James started to speak but Osman Bey held up his hand. "Now, to get down to my deal. If you give me half your winnings, I will keep quiet. If you do not, I will expose you as a cheat and tell everyone that all he has to do to reduce you to size is to use cards that are not bicycle cards. Which course do you choose?"

If Osman Bey expected Sir James to bluster, he was disappointed. To his surprise the Englishman gave him a cold smile. "You are perfectly right," he said, "and you've got yourself a deal. I will split fifty-fifty with you."

Osman Bey looked at Sir James steadily. "And one more thing. I want to know how you do it. Why it works on bicycle cards, and how you marked them, if you did."

Sir James shook his head regretfully. "That," he said, "is something you will never find out. If I told you that, you would not need me and I would not even get half my own winnings. I might as well go back to England if I tell you that."

Osman Bey grinned. "All right, just so I get my fifty per cent, you can keep your secret."

Although Sir James lived up to his deal, having to split his winnings with Osman Bey, who did nothing but collect his money and spend it on the night life of Cairo, rankled more and more every day. He had dreamed up the greatest gambling trick in all history, and he was losing half the profits to someone who didn't even know how he did it. After all, who had purchased thousands of packs of playing cards and methodically taken out the face cards and laid them out in shelves in the sun, face down in his greenhouse outside London? Not many people knew that a few hours in the hot sun will impart a very slight yellowish tinge to the back of a playing card, a tinge so slight you have to be looking hard to detect it. Gamblers referred to the trick as "sunning the deck." Being able to locate the face cards gave one a staggering advantage in most card games.

Sir James looked unhappy. What a bloody hell of a job it had been "sunning" thousands of face cards, getting them back into the right packs, and sealing them up again

with the original government seals so that everything would look legal. The rest had been easier. Exchange restrictions being what they were, importing objects into Egypt was very difficult. By selling the cards at such a low price that he took a loss on them he cornered Egypt's whole foreign exchange allocation for playing cards.

The smile returned to Sir James' face. What it boiled down to was that nearly every pack of cards in all of Egypt was one that had been "sunned" in his greenhouse outside London. Sir James looked smug. He had never had to introduce a single deck of marked cards into an Egyptian game. All the decks were marked already and waiting for him in any game he wanted to sit in on.

After a couple of months of paying tribute to Osman Bey, Sir James decided he had had enough. His marked cards were beginning to run out, and more and more often he was running into honest decks and wasting whole evenings of play. Pretty soon the games wouldn't be worth it any more, and it would be better to start operations all over again in a fresh, new country. After all, he had never told Osman Bey how he did it, so his secret was safe.

Sir James ended his stay in Egypt by making several large killings and leaving without giving Osman Bey his share.

Osman Bey, outraged at having his profits vanish, decided he *had* to find out how the bicycle cards were marked. After a month of back-breaking experimentation, he found that the reverse sides of the face cards in the bicycle decks were of a slightly yellower shade.

When Sir James, back in England, heard from some of his Egyptian friends about the killings that Osman Bey was making in card games all over Cairo, he realized his secret had been found out. He anonymously tipped off the Egyptian authorities that Osman Bey had been cheating and told about the "sunned" bicycle cards.

When Osman Bey was brought up before the law

courts, he successfully defended himself on the basis that he did not introduce the fraudulent cards into the game, had nothing to do with marking them, and was in no different position from any other player around the table. His winning, he claimed, was due to the fact that he was an excellent card player. He was completely exonerated by the courts.

When Sir James was last heard from, his greenhouse outside London was again full of trays of face cards positioned face down in the sun. He was in the process of working out his foreign-exchange problems with a very interesting South American country where the bets are high and where his title would take him into the highest circles.

THE REDEEMED CONFEDERATE BONDS
♠

Larry Gleason, one of the most skilled confidence men in the Southern states, had developed a most effective racket. He ran a veterans' home that gave old, retired war veterans the singular advantage that they could live in the same city as their lifelong friends instead of being packed off to a veterans' hospital or home in a strange locality. Gleason had just enough veterans in his home to keep his scheme from being entirely phony. And the veterans he did have received good care and were happy to be there.

The racket in Gleason's operation was that he used his veterans' home as a front for collecting large charity donations from veterans all over the state. The collections received enormously exceeded the money needed to support the few veterans he was caring for. It boiled down to the fact that he was being grossly overpaid by charitable contributions for doing something that, to the limited extent it was being done, was eminently worthwhile.

One day, while visiting a friend, Gleason was shown a $50,000 defaulted Confederate bond issued during the Civil War by the state in which he was residing. It was a beautifully engraved instrument with all the courtly legal verbiage that made it an obligation of his state.

At home that night Gleason could not get the picture of the bond out of his mind. There must be some way in which it could be redeemed at face value or somehow used as a basis for a fraud. With this in mind, the next time he saw his amused friend he gave him five dollars for the bond, on the pretense that he would frame it and hang it on the wall.

Gleason knew, of course, that after the Civil War the United States Government had passed a law that made redemption of all Confederate bonds illegal. This law was purposely passed to ruin the British investors who had, by investing in the Confederacy and financing it, greatly prolonged the Civil War. The Government wanted to establish a precedent that would make any future action of that kind very unlikely.

Finally, one night, Gleason had a brainstorm. The next morning found him furiously typing a letter to the governor of his state. He knew that the governor, a man of enormous personal wealth, was in a fight for his political life in an election that was coming up in two months. He also knew that the governor, because of his own meager war record, was particularly worried about the support he could count on from the veterans' organizations in his state.

Gleason stared at his typewriter. If he could put the governor in a position where, by using a few thousand dollars of his gigantic wealth, he could get not only favorable publicity but also the support of veterans all over the state, it would be a hard bargain for him to resist. Gleason sat thinking. He might well be able to get a very substantial monetary contribution out of the governor's personal funds for his already over-financed veterans' home.

After many drafts and much thinking Gleason sent the following letter to the Governor:

My Dear Governor Crawford:

As a contributor for many years to my veterans' home here in your capital city, I know I do not have to persuade you of the worthwhile character of our institution, and of its real contribution to the war veterans of our state. This letter is written for an entirely different and most unusual purpose.

I have inherited a $50,000 Confederate bond issued by our state during the Civil War. I know, of course, that the bond is completely worthless and that the Yankees have even passed a law forbidding our state to live up to its repayment guarantee. I also know that if some scheme could be worked out for paying this bond off, and making its redemption value available to the veterans of my veterans' home, such an action would, of course, have enormous potentialities from a publicity standpoint.

This publicity would not only stem out of the dislike most of our people have for Yankee laws and institutions, and their delight in anything that would, in effect, be slapping the Yankees in the face, but it would also be particularly newsworthy because the benefactor would be an organization dedicated to the welfare of the Confederate war veterans of the state.

Knowing, of course, that it would be exceedingly difficult to get the legislature to pass such an appropriation for one bond, because of the precedent it would set, I thought perhaps the redemption of this bond might interest you from a personal standpoint.

There is no question but that the political potential involved in such an unofficial redemption action, at this particular time, would be tremendous. Such action, expensive as it would be, would, because of its flamboyant character, undoubtedly marshal the veterans of the state behind your administration. As a contribution to our veterans' home it would of course be deductible.

I am enclosing the bond, properly endorsed over to you, in this letter.

Very truly yours,
Larry Gleason, Director
Confederate Veterans' Bide-a-Wee Home

A week later a registered letter in a heavy manila envelope came in from the governor's mansion. Gleason's hands trembled as he opened it. Inside the letter, there was another envelope, with something heavy inside. Breathlessly he read the letter.

My Dear Mr. Gleason:

I am indeed cognizant of the worthwhile activities carried on by your very prestigious Bide-a-Wee Home. I was also most intrigued by the ingenuity of thought evidenced in your letter of last Tuesday. You obviously have the makings of an extraordinarily adroit politician. I compliment you and thank you from the bottom of my heart.

I agree with you perfectly concerning the publicity potential involved in paying off your fifty-thousand dollar bond, and of the powerful influence such an action would exercise on the veterans' vote in this state. In the attached envelope you will find $50,000 in cash, together with a receipt for your signature. Good luck. It is a great pleasure to someone like myself, who can afford gestures like this one, to make even this small contribution to the excellent work you are doing.

Very sincerely yours,
Isaac Crawford
Governor

Larry Gleason's hands trembled so violently that the envelope slipped out of his hands onto the floor. Fifty thousand dollars in cash! Holy smoke! This was the biggest and easiest deal of his whole career. He snatched the envelope off the floor, ripped it open, and stared at the fifty thousand dollars it contained. They were Confederate dollars.

THE INVISIBLE COLUMNIST

There were once two great press lords who bitterly competed with each other and bitterly resented each other. Each had his powerful chain of newspapers spread across the country. Each was extremely wealthy and influential. Each was impatient with and furious over any success that came to his press lord rival. We will call them Press Lord 1 and Press Lord 2.

One day Press Lord 1 called in his managing editor, George Mayo. "George," he rumbled, "what chain of newspapers has the best gossip column in the world?"

Mayo looked at his boss in surprise. "I don't think there is any question of it, sir. We have. No one in the country can compare with Reginald Chatterwick. In fact, we are making quite a bit of money syndicating him to papers outside our areas."

Press Lord 1 glowered at his managing editor. "If there is anything I despise, it is a goddamn yes man. It's just like having virus pneumonia in your office. All a yes man does is say what he thinks you want him to say. So you never get any real information out of him. A yes man is a goddamn trap."

Mr. Mayo blanched. "I've never considered myself a yes man, sir." He looked at Press Lord 1 with frightened eyes. You never understood just where you were with a boss like this. He always said he didn't want yes men around him and yet the people who weren't yes men always seemed to get themselves fired.

"You know damn well that Chatterwick is, for the first time in his life, getting some honest-to-God competition. For ten years we've had almost a monopoly on the gossip column business. He's been so much better than anyone else that it hasn't even been a race. Now look what has happened."

"Are you referring to our competitor's new columnist, Copy Cat?"

Press Lord 1 looked at his managing editor with studied contempt. "Did you think I was referring to St. Paul the Apostle?"

Mr. Mayo blushed with embarrassment. "Copy Cat is getting quite a following," he admitted.

Press Lord 1 let out a roar that shook the pictures on the wall. "Following, my ass," he roared. "Copy Cat is turning out a lot better stuff than Chatterwick. And you know that as well as I do. Where the hell were we that we didn't find him before Press Lord 2 did?"

George Mayo shifted uneasily from foot to foot. "I'd never even heard of him before he suddenly appeared in all Press Lord 2's papers. Maybe he developed him from inside his own organization."

"Then why don't *we* develop someone like that?" Press Lord 1 glared at his managing editor. "Here one of the most valuable monopolies in the newspaper business is being snatched right out of our hands. All our competing papers, even those outside Press Lord 2's territory, are beginning to use Copy Cat. It doesn't make so much difference if he is a little better or a little worse than

Chatterwick; the unfortunate fact is that we've lost our monopoly. We've lost the squeeze that you can put on by having the only model of a product. I don't have to go into every detail with you on something like that. It would be just a hell of a lot better if *we* had discovered Copy Cat and you know it as well as I do. That's the sort of thing you are supposed to see to as managing editor."

Mr. Mayo looked at Press Lord 1 with fear-haunted eyes. "Yes, sir," he said.

"Now what I want you to do is to go out and steal Copy Cat away from Press Lord 2. Pay him whatever you have to pay him to get him." The big man paused. "But, there is one thing that I absolutely insist on. When we do get him it has got to be on a long-term contract. A contract just like Chatterwick's. When we get both of them and have our monopoly back, I don't want Press Lord 2 putting up the price and getting him back."

"Yes, sir."

"This is the most important thing right now in this shop. I want you to report progress to me every morning."

"Yes, sir."

"And one more thing: how much longer has Chatterwick's contract got to run? I don't want to get Copy Cat and then have Chatterwick snatched out from under me and have to go through the whole thing all over again."

"He's tied up tight as a drum, sir, for ten more years. If we can only get Copy Cat we've got it made."

"Good work. Now, see that you go out and get him."

A week later, Press Lord 1, his face red with anger, was reading a letter to George Mayo. "Listen to this," he shouted. He started reading the letter.

Dear Joe:

I would greatly appreciate it if you could keep your sticky, dirty, cotton-picking fingers off of my

nice clean help. You have Chatterwick. I have Copy Cat. That should be enough for even you.
Yours very truly,

Press Lord 2

Press Lord 1 glared at Mr. Mayo. "Exactly what is the meaning of this?" he demanded.

Mr. Mayo was visibly shaken. "When you told me to get Copy Cat I decided to start by writing a letter. There is no listing for Copy Cat in the telephone book or in the city directory. I had to write him at the newspaper. I couldn't think of anything else to do."

Press Lord 1 looked at his managing editor witheringly. "It never occurred to you to use the telephone?" His voice rose to a shout.

"Mrs. Smith, get me Copy Cat on the telephone," he said. A moment later Mrs. Smith appeared at the door. "Copy Cat does not receive telephone calls. There is a girl who takes his calls for him. Must be the one who types up his stuff."

"Let me speak to her," he roared. He lifted up the telephone. "Who is this speaking?" he asked.

"This is Mrs. Jones," a voice replied.

"I would like to speak to Copy Cat, please."

"I am sorry, sir, but Copy Cat never accepts telephone calls. You may give me any message you wish."

"This is Press Lord 1. I would very much like to have lunch with Copy Cat at his convenience, tomorrow, the next day, the day after that, or—in fact—any day. We can go over to the Brass Hat Club where we won't be disturbed. I have some valuable information for Copy Cat."

"I am sorry, sir, but Copy Cat always eats his lunch right here at the paper."

The big vein in Press Lord 1's temple started to throb. "I wonder if you could give me Copy Cat's home telephone number."

"I am sorry, sir, we never give out telephone numbers of our staff members. We are afraid it might subject them to harassment."

"Well then, I can write him a letter. Can you give me his home address?"

"Copy Cat prefers to have all letters addressed to him here at the newspaper."

Press Lord 1 exploded into the telephone. "Are you sure there is a Copy Cat? Are you sure that he exists?"

The voice on the phone was completely unruffled. "I can assure you, sir, that he exists. He is very much alive."

Press Lord 1 slammed down the telephone with an oath. He looked at George Mayo. "There is something extremely fishy about this whole situation, and I intend to get to the bottom of it." He carefully put the finger tips of his hands together in what looked almost like a prayer. Suddenly he looked up. "Do you remember that industrial espionage organization we hired a couple of years ago? The outfit that helped us get the governor?"

"I have been trying to forget them for two years."

"They were expensive, all right. Really threw the harpoon at us. It was worth every cent of it, though. Having the real live governor of one of the biggest states in the union safely in your pocket is something that shouldn't be underrated."

"It has been quite valuable, sir."

Press Lord 1 started tapping on the table with his gold fountain pen. "I want you to get that same man for me. The man who got the job in the governor's office and dug up all that stuff. I want him to get a job on Press Lord 2's paper and find out for us who the hell Copy Cat is, and how I can contact him. Press Lord 2 probably has the poor son of a bitch chained to a desk down in the subbasement

somewhere. I think we should regard this as a crusade. A crusade to save Copy Cat."

A shadow of amusement passed over Mayo's face. "That's very noble of you, sir."

Press Lord 1 gave him a swift, dangerous look. "Exactly what do you mean by that?"

Mayo flinched. "The interest everyone knows you always take in our working press," he stammered.

"Get that man for me today and put him to work."

A month later the industrial spy had got the information for Press Lord 1, who found out to his outrage that Copy Cat was merely his own famous columnist, Reginald Chatterwick. After trying for years to get out of his long-term, low-salaried contract with Press Lord 1, Chatterwick had finally contacted Press Lord 2 and agreed to write another column for him under the name "Copy Cat." Press Lord 2, intrigued by the financial and circulation possibilities of the idea, was even more hilariously intrigued by the chance to secretly make a fool of his old rival, Press Lord 1.

THE PASHA'S TREASURE

♠

Once, many years ago, the top-ranking Sea Pasha of the Sultan of Turkey (Five Horse Tails), Malik Pasha (The Iron Lord), decided to leave the Sultan's service and become a free-lance corsair. One day he sailed out of the Bosporus, into the Marmara Sea, and down through the Dardanelles with four of the Sultan's swiftest warships. He somehow got by the monstrous cannon guarding the Dardanelles and sailed out into the open Mediterranean.

Five years later Malik Pasha, based on an island fortress on one of the Aegean Islands, commanded a vast fleet of swift feluccas and dhows.

The Iron Lord had become the terror of the Mediterranean Sea. His stark island fortress was surrounded by vertical granite cliffs rising black out of the sea. They enclosed a spacious harbor with an entrance less than two hundred yards wide, guarded by more than a hundred enormous bronze cannon. The cannon were constantly tended by janizaries with lighted matches.

The only warship that ever attempted the passage into the Iron Lord's harbor was a British first ship of the line, dispatched by the enraged British Government to wipe him out. The mighty seventy-gun vessel was blown to smithereens when, its cannons firing, it tried to run the narrow passage.

From this impregnable bastion, the Iron Lord levied tribute on all ships except those belonging to his Lord, the Turkish Sultan, whom he still revered. When he was not capturing ships in the open Mediterranean Sea, he was raiding the coastline for treasure and women—the Greek Islands, the Italian coast near Positano and Naples. His greatest passion was women, and he collected them the way some men collect stamps. The choicest of his collection he took with him on his expeditions in a special harem felucca, a ship appointed with luxurious magnificence, which was always situated in the position of greatest safety in the middle of Malik Pasha's fleet.

Malik Pasha's special love was for blondes, a type rare in his Mediterranean area. He became increasingly intrigued by the thought that up in the North, beyond the Rock of Gibraltar, there was an island called "Engoland," where most of the women were said to have golden hair and blue eyes.

One day the Iron Lord took ten of his swiftest feluccas and, of course, the harem ship, and sailed out through the Straits of Gibraltar into the open Ocean Sea. Using a chart recovered from the English warship he had destroyed, he sailed north along the coast of Spain and finally arrived at the coast of Ireland. Sailing swiftly toward shore in the dim light of dawn, he attacked one of the Irish coastal villages. He found to his astonishment the women were not blondes but had black and brown hair and extremely deep blue eyes. He collected a few of the choicest, after an appallingly desperate battle with the local Irish peasants. What soldiers they would have made, he thought, with a little training and some modern scientific weapons!

Malik Pasha sailed north along the coast until he
saw a huge manor house perched on a hill. Obviously, he
decided, the home of the Lord of the Northern Irish area.
Again with great swiftness Malik Pasha attacked. Many of
his men were slain, but this time the Iron Lord got what
he had come for. It was the Irish Lord's beautiful eighteen-
year-old daughter. She was well worth the men he had
lost back on shore and the felucca that had been burned
in an audacious attack by the Irish rabble. Her hair was
the same color as the gold in his island treasury and her
eyes were as blue as his Mediterranean sky.

Isabelle had put up a terrible battle in his stateroom
on the harem ship, what with teeth and fingernails and
throwing everything she could lay her hands on. He had
finally tamed her, though, and the transformation had
been startling. There was something very interesting
about these Northern women and in Isabelle he had a real
collector's item. There was no doubt about that.

Then all at once the people around the Mediterranean had something new to gossip about. After all,
anything involving Malik Pasha was automatically news
because he was the man whom everyone feared. Stories
came back that now, when he was seen at sea on the
observation deck of his flagship, the Kartal (eagle), there
was always a woman with him. It was a dazzlingly beautiful woman with impossibly golden hair and blue eyes and,
most remarkable of all, no veil over her face. It actually
looked as if the Iron Lord wanted everyone to see her face.
It had been necessary, of course, the rumors said, to
change her name from Isabelle because the Prophets'
well-known dislike of the sound of bells had made the
name distasteful to the Moslems. Malik Pasha, with sar-
donic humor, had named her Buran, which meant "Black
Windstorm" in the Mongol Turkish of his Steppes ances-
tors.

The greatest gossip came, though, when the Iron

Lord left on an expedition one morning *without* his harem ship. Everyone saw him as he sat on the observation deck of the Kartal playing backgammon on an ivory inlaid board, with his lovely captive. They were clearly infatuated with each other and evidently they not only did not care who knew it. They seemed to be flaunting their infatuation before the world.

To make certain that her peaches-and-cream complexion would not be darkened by the fierce Mediterranean sun, the Iron Lord insisted that Buran always carry a green silk parasol, which had come over the caravan routes from Cathay. She carried it jauntily wherever she went and, while she was playing backgammon with her Lord, it was held respectfully over her head by a slave.

It was obvious that Malik Pasha could deny his fair captive nothing, and she became a benign influence on the bloodthirsty corsair. "Why do you burn a city when you capture it?" she protested. "Take what you want from the city and leave it to grow again like a fruit tree. You do not kill a cow every time it is milked. Keep your cities like cows and milk them every five years according to regular schedules which I will keep for you. You will do the fighting," she said, smiling radiantly at him, "and I will see that everything is kept in order."

Malik Pasha was deeply intrigued by his captive's intelligence and he grew more and more powerful and influential as her orderly arrangement of his affairs complemented his fierce bravery and organizational ability.

After one particularly bloody naval battle with the Sultan of Morocco, the awed survivors reported having seen the Iron Lord seated, during the height of the battle, on the observation platform of the Kartal with his beautiful captive, playing backgammon on the ivory inlaid board. The now-famous green silk parasol was protecting her from the sun's rays and she seemed completely oblivious, as was her Lord, to the fury and carnage of the battle that raged around them.

That was the same year that the Iron Lord electrified the Moslem world by making Buran his wife. "A sovereign Lord is supposed to have women, not a wife," his followers protested, and many predicted that evil days would follow.

Malik Pasha, however, became more and more powerful, collecting treasure of every description from all over the Mediterranean world and storing it in a secret place, which was rumored to be the richest treasure storehouse on earth.

Then one fatal day, in the midst of a minor naval engagement, a falconet ball killed Buran as she was playing backgammon with her Lord on the observation deck.

The grieving corsair, completely shattered by his loss, had her body buried in a secret place where, even after his death, it would never be desecrated by his enemies. Gradually his old fierceness returned. Again the Mediterranean was ablaze with burning cities, and thousands of men and women were sold into slavery. The harem ship was recommissioned, fitted out with lovely women and taken again wherever he went.

Gradually, as the years went by, the Iron Lord became old and feeble and finally, after a prolonged illness, he lay on his deathbed in his impregnable island fortress.

Knowing of his illness and suspecting that perhaps the iron authority of his military system had been affected by it, his enemies attacked in the dead of night. They successfully ran the blockade into his harbor fortress and captured it in the darkness with hardly a blow struck.

His enemies burst into the room where the Iron Lord lay dying. They were aghast at the possibility that he might die before revealing to them the hiding place of his vast treasure. The Iron Lord watched helplessly from his bed as the instruments were being prepared for his torture. "Tell us where you have buried your treasure," their leader urged, "and we will allow you to die in the peace which your bravery so richly deserves."

Malik Pasha's once-roaring voice was a bare whisper. "Ten leagues north of this island is another island, the Islet of Venus. In the exact center of this island is the stone structure in which I have buried my treasure."

His enemies raced pell-mell out the door and into their ships. They sailed to the Islet of Venus, a tiny island barely a quarter of a mile in diameter, and immediately found the massive stone structure at its center. They savagely slaughtered the guards and charged into the building. There was the great bronze treasure chest positioned in the exact center of the marble floor. "The Pasha's treasure," they shouted, and pried off the heavy bronze lid. They stood back aghast. "The Pasha's treasure," they whispered.

Lying in the chest was a skeleton with beautiful delicate white bones. Beside the skeleton was a green silk parasol and near its head was the ivory inlaid teakwood backgammon board with which Buran and her Lord had whiled away so many pleasant hours.

The Pasha's second, most valued treasure, the one of gold and jewels, was never found.

RED SEA DELIVERY

Leonard Quilton stopped dead in the middle of the noisy old cobblestone street and looked up at the sign. This certainly must be the most fascinating store in Tangiers if signs mean anything.

BUY YOUR COUNTERFEIT AMERICAN CURRENCY
AT
HONEST AHMED'S
LOWEST PRICES AND FINEST QUALITY
SATISFACTION GUARANTEED

Quilton stood in the middle of the street with a faint smile on his face. Where except in the Medina in Tangiers would a person ever find a sign like that? He had got himself out from under Vera for at least an hour. Until she finally tracked him down he might as well enjoy himself. He glanced up at the sign. Counterfeit American dollars right smack over the counter. That was really something.

Quilton opened the door of the little shop and stepped into the dark interior.

50

"Good morning, Mr. Quilton."

Quilton jerked his head up in surprise. He saw a large, amiable-looking Arab with a red fez on his head sitting behind the counter.

"How did you know my name?" he demanded.

The Arab laughed. "You and your wife have been wandering around the Medina for five days. Anyone who doesn't know who you are hasn't got that sense of curiosity necessary to a good tradesman."

Quilton laughed. "I'm interested in that sign outside your store. How can you advertise counterfeit American currency for sale that way without getting arrested by the authorities?"

The Arab got to his feet. "First, let me introduce myself." He inclined his head respectfully. "I am the 'Honest Ahmed' mentioned in the sign, and the reason the authorities do not do anything about me is that there are no authorities. Tangiers is one of those political anachronisms, an absolutely free city, created by the Franco-Spanish Convention of 1912. As long as we pay our taxes and as long as we don't have too much civil commotion, everyone lets us alone. It is the quintessence of that old law of *caveat emptor* that you have so completely repudiated in your American society."

Honest Ahmed smiled at Quilton. "People buy their counterfeit dollars from me because they are better counterfeits than my competitors'. They are harder to detect and they are also cheaper. It's just the old case of honesty being the best policy."

Quilton stared at the Arab. Honesty the best policy! "I'll bet our Treasury Department takes a dim view of that."

"No doubt it does. We get our protests, but," he gestured towards the wastepaper basket, "we just throw them into the round file." The tassel on his red fez flopped over to the other side. "There is one big rule that eats up all the other rules in the Medina. That rule is that *anything* can be bought and sold in the Medina. That is, in fact, the main strength of the Medina. It is the world's only absolutely free market. You can buy and sell women, dope, stolen goods, illegal medicines, human lives, deadly poisons. Almost anything that has value can be purchased in the Medina."

"Did you say human lives?"

Honest Ahmed motioned Quilton to a chair. "I certainly did. After all, they are just another type of commodity. You can have someone murdered here for a price, or you can buy or sell someone for a price."

"How can you buy or sell someone?"

"I had an interesting case the other day. A man had a wife whom he had got tired of. She was very beautiful but he did not want her any more. He wanted to marry someone else. I sold her for him."

"Sold her!"

"Sold her. I just acted as a purchasing agent for one of the sultans in the Trucial States. I got the happy husband two thousand dollars for her and all I had to do was load her on an ocean dhow for F.O.B. delivery at a Red Sea port." Honest Ahmed smiled a winning smile. "The sultans down there really are rascals. They are forever building up their portfolios of women. It's very much like you American businessmen buying commodities as a hedge against inflation."

"But didn't the wife have anything to say about this?"

"Exactly who would she say it to? Her husband brought her right here to the store. I paid him two thousand dollars that, incidentally, were not counterfeit and we just tied her up and loaded her on the ship."

"An American woman can't just disappear like that."

"Well, here is one who did. Her husband just told the authorities the truth. He said they got separated in the Medina and that he has not seen her since."

"How did you know the sultan wanted a woman he hadn't even seen yet?"

"It's like being someone's agent in anything else. You've got to know your customer's tastes. And even if I make a mistake occasionally there is always enough profit margin to cover my loss. After all, an attractive woman always has a resale value. Exactly like a motorcar." Honest Ahmed hesitated. "I know that you will be amused by this and take it in the spirit in which it is said, but I can tell you that I really drooled right into my coffee when I saw your wife."

Quilton looked up sharply. "*My* wife! Why?"

"Because of that extraordinary red hair and her very white complexion. I've got one client who would go absolutely wild over that. I would cheerfully pay three thousand dollars for her, with no questions asked, because I could easily unload her at twice that."

"Unload her?"

♠

Two days later, Quilton was arguing with the captain of their cruise ship. "But you absolutely can't leave Tangiers without my wife," he shouted. "She's gone! Vanished into the Medina. For all I know she's in someone's harem!"

The captain looked at Quilton with compassion. "I know exactly how you feel, Mr. Quilton. I lost my own wife last year and life has not been the same since. I know you will understand though, Mr. Quilton. There is absolutely nothing we can do about it. It is as if she had fallen overboard at night. We have some three hundred passengers on board who have contracted to see the Mediterranean. If I break our schedule, I'd get lawsuits all over the place. In view of the mitigating circumstances, I will be glad to refund your fare from here on so you can stay and look for her."

A week later, Quilton was on his way back to the United States. As his plane lifted from the airport, he felt an enormous load lifting from his shoulders. That was certainly the quickest way anyone had ever figured out to unload a bitchy wife. Unloading the worst shrew anyone had ever been married to. Vera had been the all-out triple-threat genius in the bitch department. One thing he could guarantee: he would never look at another red-haired woman as long as he lived. That unfortunate sheik was going to have his hands full, all right. The poor bastard thought he was just buying another woman for his harem. That was the biggest laugh of the Moslem calendar year. Just wait until Vera got her claws into the poor son of a bitch. Honest Ahmed had said that a Red Sea sheik can take care of any woman. Quilton shook his head in amusement. He would certainly give anything to be able to watch that operation.

Quilton looked out the window of the rapidly rising plane and pressed his hand against his wallet. And on top of all that, actually getting $3,000 for her. Like being paid for getting over tuberculosis. He smiled happily. He would never forget that look she gave him as they grabbed her. It was while Ahmed was paying out the $3,000.

Quilton closed his eyes happily. Ahmed was an amazingly versatile chap. When Quilton had told him about Vera's insurance, that he actually needed a woman's body to identify so he could collect on her policy when he got back to the United States, Ahmed had produced a body on twelve hours' notice. The hair was dyed red and features mutilated so that no one could deny his identification.

Quilton settled back in the comfortable seat. There certainly was a whale of a lot to be said for a laissez-faire economy. No doubt about that. He had had to pay Ahmed $100 for producing the body but that was the bargain of all time. He was going to collect at least $40,000 on Vera's insurance policy. Quilton sat bolt upright. He had completely forgotten the double indemnity clause for that sort of violent death. He was going to get $80,000.

A year later, Quilton was relaxing at his New York club. It had been the happiest year of his life, no doubt about that. The first rule of having a happy life was to be sure that there was no one the slightest bit like Vera in it. Life with her had been exactly like that old saw about hitting yourself on the head because it felt so good when you stopped. Life had certainly felt damn good for a year and no one had suspected one single thing. Everyone was sorry for him and he was actually up to his navel in beautiful women. Even the insurance company had come through nobly once they got the report from the consular officials. Quilton laughed softly to himself. From what Honest Ahmed told him, the Red Sea sheiks must be real bastards as far as women are concerned. It would certainly be nice to know what the sheik had to do to cut someone like Vera down to size.

"There is a gentleman outside to see you, sir."

Quilton looked up at the waiter. "I expected no one. Are you sure it's for me?"

"Very certain, sir. He even wrote your name out on a piece of paper. He said he has been sent to you by someone by the name of Honest Ahmed."

An electric shock of cold fear lifted Quilton out of his chair.

An hour later in a secluded corner of the club's bar, Quilton knew there was no way he could get out of the trip. His Arab visitor smiled at him politely. "Honest Ahmed been contacted very important people, very interested disappearance Mrs. Quilton. Honest Ahmed decided if you not come over to Tangiers to help him fix situation, will be forced to get immunity for himself by telling whole story and advising insurance company. They would dig up body, make dental identification and find body not Mrs. Quilton."

Quilton felt his scalp moving on the back of his head. That would be the end of him, all right.

"Ahmed say, necessary have fifty thousand dollars to close mouths. Says if you not in Tangiers within week will be forced to get immunity self by telling about you."

Three days later, Quilton walked into Honest Ahmed's shop in the Medina. In his brief case was fifty thousand dollars in cash. He did not acknowledge the Arab's polite salutation. "What in hell has happened?" he demanded harshly.

The Arab shrugged expressively. "Nothing has happened, Marshallallah. I only wanted you here in my shop. I have just sold you to my new client, the Sultan of Aquat."

Quilton heard the great bronze door clang behind him and he whirled around. There was a man standing there with a wicked-looking gun pointed at his middle. He slowly raised his hands.

Honest Ahmed shook his head reproachfully. "Resistance is useless, Mr. Quilton," he said. Your only course is to submit to Kismet, the fate which Allah has in store for you. We must all do that, Mr. Quilton."

Quilton's voice came out in a high screech and then subsided. "I don't understand," he quavered.

"It is most simple, my friend. My new client, the Sultan of Aquat, is a very modern man. He has even tried to put plumbing facilities in his palace but his favorite wife is the old-fashioned type and will not allow this. For one single minute. She likes the old-fashioned ways. They have finally compromised by deciding to purchase a handsome American man for the latrine detail. Some man who can work hard in the latrines and take a great deal of punishment."

Honest Ahmed spread his hands expressively. "You

know, my friend, how the *nouveau riche* are. The Sultan must live up to his new title by doing things extravagantly. Having a handsome, expensive American man on the latrine detail will be an enormous status symbol. He may not have a gold-plated Rolls Royce like some of his friends but he will have an educated, top-echelon American cleaning out his toilets."

"Also," Honest Ahmed coughed apologetically, "the Sultan's wife was particularly anxious to get you. She used to be *your* wife, Vera, and knows that you can be depended upon for jobs like that."

THE BITER BIT

♠

Lomax knew he was playing against the first team when two white chips came rolling across the table toward him. He looked questioningly at his hundred-dollar bill. The banker's gray eyes twinkled. "The white chips are fifty dollars apiece," he said.

Lomax hesitated a moment. "I guess I'd better raise my stake then." He opened his wallet and counted out twenty five-hundred-dollar bills and pushed them across the table. There was a thin smile on his face. "How much is the limit?" he asked.

Six pairs of eyes looked at him incredulously. Again the banker's eyes twinkled. "We've never had any limit at the Alamo Club," he said. "Of course, if things get too tough, we divide the pot." He doubled up his fist and hit the man next to him affectionately on the shoulder. "Otherwise Roper here might toss in a billion dollars and freeze us poor millionaires out of the pot entirely."

Roper joined in the laughter. "We've been playing together over ten years and I haven't been able to freeze anybody out yet."

Lomax pulled in his ten-thousand-dollar pile of chips. He had come a helluva long way in the last twenty years. And the whole twenty-year payoff was going to be right here, tonight! He let his eyes wander over the sumptuous appointments of the Club. There was literally nothing in the whole club that could be bettered as far as quality or expense went. The lovely Mahal rug, the paintings that were obviously Rembrandts, the obsequious and magnificently-appointed waiters, the obviously authentic fifteenth-century Italian furniture. Lomax smiled a slow, contented smile. The Club had everything necessary to make it look exactly what it was, the Club that was reputed to have the wealthiest membership of any club on earth. It had taken him over five years to wangle an invitation to play and he was going to make the most of it.

Lomax looked at the hard-bitten, sunburned men around the table. These tough Texans didn't look too much like the softies he had been bottom dealing to on the transatlantic liners—the people you could push over for a few thousand dollars in a crooked poker game, who didn't have the guts to complain too much about it. If this bunch of meat burners ever caught you cheating, they'd probably shoot you dead over the poker table and have the servants dump your body in the incinerator.

Lomax felt an inner glow of satisfaction. Nobody had caught him cheating yet. And nobody was ever going to. Even this sharp-eyed bunch. Most low-echelon card sharks could deal off the bottom of the deck. A much lesser number of "specialists" could "second deal" convincingly. Only a handful anywhere, though, could actually "middle deal" out of the center of the pack.

Lomax looked arrogantly around the table. He not only could do them all at once, and that was unique, but he had all those special tricks he had developed over the years that nobody else could do at all. Lomax shuffled the cards with studied clumsiness. In fact, he was probably one of the two or three men on earth who could actually deal a person any hand he wanted to out of a stone cold deck.

Lomax started dealing out the cards. He'd deal a few honest hands to allay everybody's suspicions and then he'd really jam the harpoon into them. All those hundreds of hours' practice in front of the mirror had finally paid off. He could always tell a card shark by the cadence of his deal. He would defy anyone, though, to do that with him. If the tape recorder couldn't detect the slightest difference in sound when *he* played it back, who in hell could?

Of one thing he was sure! When this night was over, he'd never have to do another lick of work in his whole life. It would be the Riviera for him, all right, on the next boat. And he'd never have to look another pack of cards in the face. He'd line up a nice little racing stable of the loveliest women he could lay his hands on and—Lomax's smile came back—he would spend all his time laying his hands on them.

Half an hour later, Lomax decided to snap the trap. He'd been patiently setting it for twenty years and now was the time. His first ten thousand was gone, mostly in antes, he thought ruefully, but a few good hands would not only fix that up, they would also fix up the rest of his life.

Lomax counted fifty thousand dollars out of his billfold and shoved it across the table at the banker. He breathed on his hands. He could not afford to have his fingers too slippery for the biggest deal of his life. He started dealing. Had to play it conservatively, nothing flamboyant with a bunch of carnivores like this. As he dealt the cards his mind tabulated everything with the accuracy of a computer. His skilful fingers spotted the cards in their correct places within the perfectly even rhythm of his deal. He dealt the billionaire three fives and the banker four hearts and a spade. He gave himself two sevens. Not high enough to be suspicious but it would really bring in the money.

The other four players got the natural run of the cards as they came.

The banker opened with a five-thousand-dollar bet. The billionaire, Roper, raised it five thousand and Lomax raised it another five thousand. No use being a hog. To Lomax's surprise, the man on the right, whose hand he had not stacked, bumped it up to twenty thousand. Lomax looked at him in astonishment. What the hell did *he* have? Just the natural run of the cards. Eighty thousand dollars in the pot and they hadn't even drawn their cards yet.

The banker took one card and Lomax gave him the ten of hearts. Having a heart flush would put gas in that buggy. The billionaire got two tens for a five over ten full house. The unknown on his right asked for one card and Lomax gave him the fourth ten. Lomax dealt himself three jacks for a jack high full house. He looked at the unknown. With only one of three tens and three jacks out, there just wasn't much he could have. It had to be a bluff, all right.

The others checked to Lomax. He hesitated a moment and then shoved what was left of his fifty-thousand-dollar pile into the center of the table. Both his opponents called.

Lomax felt his heart pounding. The pot had almost a quarter of a million dollars in it. He put down his jacks over sevens. His opponent (the billionaire) laid down his fives over tens and the banker, his heart flush. To his surprise the unknown put down the 2-4-6-8-10 of spades. He had been bluffing on absolutely nothing at all.

Lomax chuckled as he reached for the pot. "That bluff took real guts," he said. "It damn near scared me out." The unknown was smiling, too. "It would have been better for you if it had," he said amiably. "It's my pot!"

"Your pot?"

"I have a General Sam Houston."

"A General Sam Houston? I've never heard of it."

"A 2-4-6-8-10 of any suit is a General Sam Houston. It always beats anything."

Lomax got halfway to his feet. Something in the others' eyes told him he had better sit down. He turned questioningly to the others around the table. "Is this a joke or something? I've never heard of a General Sam Houston."

The others all nodded in agreement. "That's the way we've played for twenty years—Alamo Club Rules. When you play with us, you've got to play our rules."

Lomax sank back in his chair. His mind was going like a computer. Sixty thousand dollars vanished into thin air. He saw his opponent pulling in the two-hundred-thousand-dollar pot. Lomax closed his eyes spasmodically. He had exactly fifty thousand dollars left in his billfold, the tail end of all his life savings from numberless transatlantic voyages. Slowly he took it out and threw it on the table. Above all he couldn't afford to offend anyone now. The banker shoved over the chips and Lomax stared at them. If those were the rules, who could adapt to them any better than he could?

Lomax let two deals go by and then dealt what he knew would be the greatest hand of his life. It might well be the greatest hand of anyone's life. He dealt a potential straight flush to the man who had gotten the "General Sam Houston," three queens to the banker, a pair of jacks to the billionaire, and two potential flushes and an outside straight to the others. He dealt himself a potential "General Sam Houston," 2-4-6-8 of clubs.

Lomax was amused at the low bets. Operation Cobra. Everyone was lying low—herding in the suckers for the killing.

After the draw, Lomax had a "General Sam Houston"

and the others had a straight flush, four queens, a jack-high full house, a straight and two flushes. Lomax almost laughed out loud when everyone checked to him. Perfect poker faces—no one acted as if they had anything at all. And they would find that they really didn't. He pushed in his whole pile. "It's all I've got," he said.

The billionaire looked disappointed. "I'd like to really take you boys up on this one," he admitted. "Out of courtesy to our guest, though, and so we won't have to split the pot, I'm only going to 'see.'" There was a reluctant murmur of agreement around the table. Everyone "saw" and put down their hands. The banker put down his four queens. The billionaire, Roper, laid down his jack-high full house. The man who had beaten him with the "General Sam Houston" happily laid down his straight flush and the straight and two flushes stayed in, too. There were three hundred and fifty thousand dollars piled up in the center of the table. Lomax tried to control the almost spastic trembling of his fingers. "I guess my 'General Sam Houston' wins," he said, reaching for the pot.

The man with the straight flush looked at Lomax open-mouthed. "You've been an exceedingly interesting player to tangle with," he said admiringly, "and you're going to be even more so when you learn our rules here in the Alamo Club. One of our oldest rules is 'no more than one "General Sam Houston" in any one evening.'"

THE WOMAN POWDER

♠

Joe Dillon looked sourly across the table at his companion. It certainly hadn't taken him long to find out that Frank was quite a character. A pain in the bucket in a lot of ways but a big relief after some of those other friends of his. The ones who were always sitting around waiting for him to pick up the check. The big trouble, though, was Frank being such a terrific torpedo. It made him feel let down, somehow. He had always been the ladies' man to end all ladies' men himself, in his salad days. It was one hell of a note that those days finally seemed to be over. It probably just boiled down to pure jealousy. Dillon sighed. Watching Frank wrap those lovely chicks around his thumb certainly gave him a yen for the old days. He was going to have to get used to it, though. It was just one of the perquisites of youth.

A woman, obviously the most attractive one in the bar, was leaning over Frank as if she wanted to eat him up. Frank, the son of a bitch, was playing it just as cold as a cucumber, and why the hell wouldn't he, with a woman falling all over him that way. He just sat there and sipped his whisky and soda. That was just the way he used to play women when he was in Frank's shoes.

The girl reached over and kissed Frank on the top of the head and they both watched her go back to her table. Her date was looking pretty grim. He looked as if he wanted to smash up the joint. Joe Dillon looked at his friend. "How the hell old are you," he asked? "My sixty-five years are really beginning to weigh on me, particularly when I see a woman as excited about someone as that one obviously is about you."

Frank smiled uneasily. "I don't usually tell people my age because it always leads to a lot of horsing around and questions and explanations. I'll tell you though. I was seventy-three the first of last month."

Joe looked at his friend steadily. "Frank," he said, "you're a goddamn liar. If you can prove to me that you are over forty-five, I'll give you a thousand dollars."

Frank stared back at him across the table. "If I was interested in money, which I'm not, I'd really give you the shaft on that one, but I couldn't do that to a friend." He took his wallet out of his pocket. "Here, look at my driver's license."

Dillon looked at the license and back at his friend. "If I didn't have it in my hand I wouldn't believe it. Hell, you are actually eight years *older* than I am and you look and act about twenty years younger. What the hell sort of a life have you been leading?"

An uneasy look came over Frank Schwartz's face. "I've been doing it the hard way, lots of whisky, lots of staying up nights, lots of women, four packs of cigarettes a day," he smiled. "It all makes Frank a high-echelon sex box."

Dillon tapped his fingers on the table. Frank's answer was just as phony as a fifteen-dollar bill. One thing about being the president of a big international export-import company, you could sniff out a phony answer five miles upwind. Frank had fumbled around with that answer as if it was red hot. Even now he looked like a kid with his hand in the cookie jar. Frank had some sort of a secret all right, goat glands, marijuana sandwiches, something as queer as Dick's hatband. It was going to be fun weaseling it out of him.

Dillon looked at Frank appraisingly. It was a bit out of his line, dealing with a person who was not interested in money, but that was just another adaptation. What all life was, really—a series of adaptations. He sipped his drink. On a fellow like Frank a fellow had to use the old deep-sea fishing technique. Throw out some bait and they swallow it every time. The bigger the bait the bigger the fish. Or you get them drunk. What the hell kind of a fish couldn't you catch if you could get him drunk first?

Dillon ordered two more drinks. "Frank," he said, "sometimes I actually feel like committing suicide." Frank jerked up his head. "Suicide?"

"Yes, suicide. I know it sounds ridiculous with all the money I have and the social position, health, and everything else, but really, you know, those are just digested pleasures. They never make up for the ones you haven't got."

Frank looked incredulous. "But what the hell pleasures haven't you got? Hell, if you have all that money you can buy just about anything you can possibly want."

"There is one thing you can't buy," Dillon said. "That's the kind of woman I want. The ones who aren't available to everyone else. I wouldn't give you ten cents for the most beautiful prostitute on earth because she literally wouldn't do me any good. The only kind of women I am interested in are the ones who are physically attracted to me." Dillon looked unhappily across the table. "And there don't seem to be any more like that. I would give anything to find a woman who felt about me just like that girl a few minutes ago obviously felt about you. She certainly made one thing obvious. If you took her upstairs to bed you would be doing her the biggest favor in the world." He looked at Frank appraisingly. "And I bet you could, too."

Frank glared back at him indignantly. "Well, what the devil makes you think I couldn't? As soon as I finish this drink I intend to do just that. In fact, I have already lined up a room in the hotel upstairs."

Dillon took a big gulp of his drink. "That's what really gets me. Here you are, eight years older than I am. I've got to the point where if I got one like that upstairs I am not sure I'd know what to do with her." He looked at Frank mournfully. "I guess if I didn't have you to compare myself with I would feel all right."

Frank looked acutely unhappy. He seemed to be wrestling with himself over some problem. Dillon ordered another drink. The fellow probably had some sort of new medical treatment, monkey glands or that Swiss doctor everyone was talking about, some new formula. Frank was always traveling around the Middle East and the Far East. From the looks of him he must have gotten hold of something. Maybe he had pulled a Faust and sold his soul to the devil somehow. Dillon grinned. Boy, would he ever sell his in two minutes flat. "What I wouldn't give," he said, "to be in your shoes for just one day."

Frank jerked up his head. "You can," he said, "if you promise not to ask me any questions and if you give me your everlasting word of honor you'll never ask me to do it again."

"Are you kidding?" Joe asked.

"No, I am not kidding one damn bit and you'll find it out soon enough for yourself. You aren't going to believe me, but I don't give a damn whether you do or not. In fact, I wouldn't even be telling you this if I wasn't drunk and if you hadn't been such a hell of a nice guy."

Frank took another gulp of his drink. "Now hold on

to the edge of your seat and I'll tell you something that will give you the biggest laugh of the year." He paused. "You won't be laughing one damned bit tomorrow, though, and that's what worries me. I am only doing this on one condition, and that is that you give me your word of honor that you will never mention the matter to me again."

Dillon tried to keep from laughing. "It sounds pretty cloak and daggerish, but I agree."

"I'm sure I told you, Joe, that on my last trip to the Far East I got into Tibet. It turned out to be a hell of a lot more exciting than I thought it was going to be because I got there just as the Chinese Communists started invading the country. Pouring in like locusts all over the place. I did one of the head lamas of the country one of the greatest favors you can do a man. I saved his life."

Frank sipped his drink. "My chartered plane was already loaded up, with the props turning. The Commies were just about to capture the son of a bitch when I did something extremely foolish. I unloaded a case of the most priceless artifacts you could possibly imagine so I could take this fellow and his girl friend on my plane. I just dumped the treasures out on the ground because at that altitude the plane couldn't take off with both.

"The old boy got on with his bright yellow robes and with the prettiest little chick you ever saw in your life— eyes slanted up like a Chinese doll. He knew what a favor I was doing him, off-loading the crate of artifacts that way, because he had got them for me and I had paid plenty for them. They were ten times as valuable now that the Communists were taking over.

"As soon as we were airborne he turned to me. 'You have done a noble and generous thing,' he told me gravely, 'and you will find it is the wisest thing you have ever done. You did it out of charity, but no man will ever have been rewarded better for his charity than you will be.' He looked at me with those luminous yellow eyes. 'How old do you think I am?' he demanded.

"I looked at his jet black hair and his erect powerful figure. I thought of his endurance on the hunting trip we had taken together and the light, swift way he had lifted up that chick of his and put her in the plane. We were flying high now and the Communist menace was behind us and the young chick laughed up at me. 'You will never in the world guess,' she said, 'but I will give you a hint. Every single night of the year he wants to make love to me, and every single day, as well.'

"I looked at the lama carefully. I knew one thing, you didn't get to be the head man in that league and have the right to wear those yellow robes until you had got right along in years. He didn't look a month older than forty-five, though, so that is what I guessed.

"'You're not bad,' he said, smiling. 'In fact, you are only a little more than fifty years off. In less than two months I will be having my ninety-fifth birthday.'

"I decided to play along with the gag and turned to the chick. 'How old are you?' I asked. To my surprise the corners of her mouth turned down and she burst into a storm of tears. 'It doesn't work on women,' she wailed. 'When I am an old wrinkled hag of seventy, he'll look just exactly the way hc does now.'

"I looked at the lama and suddenly I knew that this was no gag at all.

"The lama produced two gold boxes. 'One is for me,' he said, 'and the other is now for you.'

"My box contained hundreds of tiny gelatin capsules the size of vitamin pills. They were filled with a bright green powder.

"'The capsules are your American scientific technology,' the lama said. 'The green powder inside them is our ancient magic of Tibet. It is the male principle in concentrated form. Every man has it to a certain extent, some a

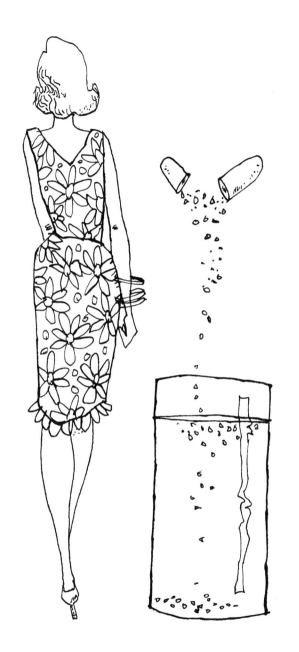

lot more than others. It is the thing that attracts females to him. The thing that enables him to satisfy them and make them happy.'

"The lama's yellow eyes looked sad. 'You queer barbarians with your scientific technology will discover it soon enough yourselves, and you will have all sorts of scientific explanations for it. Already I know what they will be. "It is an electro-magnetic vibration," your wise men will say, "like the firefly flashing and attracting its mate. His radiations are long enough in wave length so that we can actually see them. The human male flashes just the same way but his vibrations are too short to see. They are in the invisible band. Gradually as age overtakes a man, he loses this power and soon death claims him. This power is the essence of life itself." '

"The lama held up one of the pills. 'When you feel you need one of these, pull the little capsule apart and drop the green powder into a glass of water and drink it. For two hours no woman on earth will be able to resist you. Then the effect will vanish and you will return to your former condition. Every time you take a pill, though, the period will be a little bit longer. I now take only one pill a year, on my birthday.'

"The yellow eyes stared at me fixedly. 'You have given me my life so I have given back to you five hundred years of it. May the world remain undestroyed until you have consumed your last pill.' "

Frank Schwartz looked at Dillon. "So, now you have heard my secret and you are being polite like the gentleman you are and pretending to believe me. I am going to do something I have never done before and will never do again. The pills are in my safety deposit vault, but I have one in my room, the yearly one I was planning to take myself next week. I am going to give it to you on two conditions."

Dillon looked at Frank suspiciously. "What conditions?"

"You've got to take the pill right in front of me. I don't want anyone else having this stuff analyzed. Also, you've got to promise you will never ask for another one *ever* the rest of your life."

Dillon tried to keep from laughing. "I'll play along with the gag," he said. "I promise never to ask you for another one."

"You're going to find that last promise hard to keep." Frank got up. "The shows got out about half an hour ago. In the next half hour you'll find as many beautiful women in this bar as anywhere in the city on short notice. While I am getting the pill you pick one out. The one that intrigues you the most. I'll soon show you whether this is a gag or not. Try to get a chick who doesn't have too formidable a boy friend. Remember you've just got two hours. You're looking for a bed, not a fight. In the meantime, order us a couple more drinks."

The drinks had barely arrived when Frank was back. "Have you picked one?" he asked.

"All the really beautiful-looking ones seem to have great big formidable-looking torpedoes in tow. How in the hell do I go about this?"

Frank was balancing a bright, green capsule in the palm of his hand. "You won't have to do anything but look at her. If you can catch a woman's eye across the room, and mentally order her to come over to you, she'll come waggling over like a goddamn French poodle."

Dillon looked at his friend with undisguised suspicion. "Are you sure you aren't just feeding me a great big line of crap?"

Frank glared back at him with exasperation. "You are doing your best to cheat yourself out of something very special and I don't see why I should give a damn whether you do or not." He pointed toward the bar.

"Which do you think is the most beautiful woman at the bar?"

"No problem about that. The third one from this end."

"All right, watch this." Frank went around to the other side of the bar and caught the girl's eye. She looked blankly at him. He returned to his seat next to Dillon. When they looked up the girl had turned around and was staring at him. Frank stared back. "Now watch her come trotting over," he said.

The girl's lips were parted in obvious indecision. She looked at Frank again. She hesitated a moment with a queer look on her face. Suddenly she got up and came straight over to their table. She hung over Frank. "I've seen you before somewhere, haven't I?" she stammered.

"No," Frank said, "but you are going to see a lot of me from now on and I am going to see even more of you." He smiled. "And I mean that in more than one way. As soon as you can get rid of your boy friend, come back. I'll be waiting for you."

"I'm engaged to him," she whispered, "but I'll be back. What is your name?"

Frank looked her up and down arrogantly. He made it obvious that he was undressing her. "Exactly what difference does that make?" he asked.

The girl blushed crimson. "I guess it doesn't make any difference," she said. She returned to her date and they could see that a violent argument was taking place. She was putting her hand on her head as if she had a headache. A few minutes later they left together.

Dillon looked at Frank incredulously. "That's the goddamnedest thing I've ever seen. Will she come back?"

Frank laughed. "If I was a betting man and interested in money, which I'm not the slightest, I'd bet you five hundred against one dollar that she'll be back here within an hour." Frank fondled the green pill. "I can tell you one thing. When she does come back, I am going to lose all my interest in you. So if you want to try this thing out, we'd better get started right away." He pulled the transparent capsule apart and the green powder fell into Dillon's drink. "Drink it down," Frank snapped. "It takes about ten minutes for it to take effect. You have ten minutes to pick your chick."

Dillon drank down his drink and started looking around. He certainly felt like a goddamn fool, but what the hell did he have to lose?

The men discussed the various women one by one around the room. Dillon knew it must be his imagination, but he seemed to feel a strange new power taking possession of him. One girl turned around while he was looking at her and rose half to her feet. Frank smiled grimly. "You are just about ready, old man," he said. "Did you see that last one rise to the bait?"

Dillon and Frank looked up. There was a commotion at the door. Dillon gawked. Standing in the door arguing with the doorman was one of the most beautiful women he had ever seen. She belonged in the place about as much as Queen Elizabeth did. She had tears in her eyes and she was in real trouble about something, no doubt about that. She was wringing her hands. "If you won't fix it, who will?" she was asking the doorman. Dillon could hear his reply. "I'm no garage mechanic. I wouldn't fix a flat tire for all the tea in China."

Dillon stared at her and suddenly she looked around. Their glances met. She stood there frozen in the middle of her sentence staring at him.

"That," said Dillon to Frank, "is the woman I want. And I don't think she has anyone with her."

The woman stood there, the tears still glistening in her eyes, looking at Dillon. Suddenly she left the doorman and came across the floor towards them. She seemed to be in a daze as they met in the middle of the room.

"The second I saw you across the room," she said, "I knew you would help me."

Dillon handed the doorman a twenty-dollar bill. "Get someone to fix her tire right away," he rasped. "If it isn't done in fifteen minutes, I'll buy this place just so I can fire you."

The doorman dove for the telephone and Dillon helped the girl into his car. He plunked himself down beside her. He stared at her. What a dish. Coal black hair and exotic green eyes. That fur coat must have cost $10,000. And those green emerald earrings that matched those surprising green eyes were real, no doubt about that. His eyes devoured her. And her dress was an original Dior, no doubt about that, either. Who in God's name was this beautiful woman sitting there looking at him as if she would like to have him for dinner? Even in his salad days he had never seen anything like this.

"Who are you?" he asked.

The girl looked at Dillon and suddenly blushed bright crimson. "I don't think I'll tell you," she said slowly. "When I look at you, such strange thoughts go through my head. I seem to be under some sort of a spell. Maybe after tonight I'll be ashamed to have you know my name." She put her hand on his arm. "Aren't you ever going to kiss me?"

Fifteen minutes later they were out at his house and ten minutes after that they were in bed together. An hour and a half later Dillon was looking down at her as she lay asleep. One thing he was sure of, he had never seen as wild a one as that. He looked at her, puzzled. Nor one so innocent. His frown deepened. Nor one so uninhibited. She acted just like a very modest virgin who had had some sort of a satanic spell cast over her. So that's what Frank's male principle did. No wonder Frank was such a god-damned torpedo. An artificial torpedo, really, powered by green-powder magic. Frank had made him promise he would never talk about it again, but how in the hell could he not? This was the substance of life itself. Nothing—his money, his friends—nothing was worth as much as being able to do something like this whenever you wanted to.

Dillon saw that the girl's eyes were open and that she was staring back at him. There was a look of stark horror on her face. "Who are you?" she demanded. "And why am I here?" There was a mounting hysteria in her voice. "Why am I here and who are you?" she repeated. She jumped out of bed and tried to cover herself with her hands.

"They aren't big enough to cover much," he said gently. He started to get up. There was a wild, insane look in her eyes. "If you put one foot out of that bed, I'll scream the whole house down," she cried. In a moment she was dressed and gone.

Dillon dressed, jumped in his car and drove down to the hotel. The doorman was apologetic. "She came in about ten minutes ago and drove away. No, I don't know who she was. No, I don't remember her license number."

Dillon looked at his watch. It was two and one-half hours since he had taken the pill. One thing was sure. Once she came out from under that spell, she really came out with no two ways about it. "Is Frank Schwartz still around?"

The doorman shook his head. "A very sharp looking chick, the one that left earlier in the evening, came in about an hour ago and took him away with her. She acted like somebody he had known for many years."

Dillon swore savagely under his breath. The son of a bitch had known her for all of forty-five seconds. Maybe the Tibetans were a bunch of slant-eyed, moon-faced greasy jerks, but they sure had something in that green powder.

The next night Joe Dillon and Frank Schwartz were drinking at the same bar. Frank sipped his drink. "I hope

things turned out as well for you as they did for me last
night."

Dillon looked at his friend sourly. "You know
damned well how things turned out." He put his hand on
his companion's arm. "I know, Frank, that I promised you
up and down that I wouldn't talk about this again if you
gave me one of those capsules . . ."

"And," said Frank, "I am going to hold you strictly to
your promise. You can talk all you want about the girl and
how much fun you had, but when you start talking about
the pills I am going to get right up and leave you and you
will never see me again—ever."

Dillon looked at his friend aggressively. "I am offering you a half million dollars cold cash for one hundred of
those pills."

Frank looked at his friend as if he were looking at a
child. "Have you gone crazy or something? No woman is
worth it, and besides that would leave me barely enough
for myself. Besides, how in the hell could you make a
legal contract? I don't know what the hell is in the pills
any more than you do. It may be Tibetan horse manure
for all I know. You could take my pills and then sue me to
get your half million dollars back. Wouldn't I sound like a
real feather merchant in a court of law? Trying to prove
that 100 green pills I got from a fakir in Tibet were worth
a half a million dollars when I didn't even know what was
in them? Hell, they would probably indict me for practicing medicine without a license. Besides, Joe, I just don't
need a half million dollars. It's naturally always nice to
have an extra half million in your pocket, but frankly I'd
rather have my pills."

Joe was very patient. Thank God, at least, that
Frank had not terminated the conversation. "Things like
that are just technicalities that can be solved by a lawyer.
Hell, we can put the pills in escrow, not to be delivered to
me until you get the half million dollars in cash. I can pay

you the half-million dollars for something else and the pills can be something incidental. We will say in the contract that they are not for me to take, but they are for me to have analyzed. If I can have one analyzed, maybe we can get a million pills out of it."

Two weeks later, Dillon was sitting in the same bar. The women looked particularly lovely tonight, he thought as he took the little green pill out of his pocket. Somehow or another he had to find his girl of the other night though. There must be some way to trace her. He would just keep coming here until she showed up. In the meantime, some other girl would just have to pinch-hit.

He separated the halves of the capsule and the green powder cascaded down into his drink. There was one chick over there that didn't look half bad. He would wait for about fifteen minutes for the pill to take effect and then would make a bombing run on her.

Dillon downed his drink with satisfaction. Frank was a queer duck all right. An independent son of a bitch. But even he had cocked an ear when he smelled that half million dollars. A half million dollars was a lot of money, but it didn't make that much difference to him, and look what he had got for it. A million nights just like the one he had the other night. One of the biggest bargains in history. Frank was actually mad at him after they made the transaction. He said it was the damndest fool thing he had ever done. He would get over it, though.

Dillon looked at his watch. It was just about that time. He stared at the girl. One good thing about this one, her boy friend looked like a goddamned Mediterranean fruit fly. Certainly wouldn't have any trouble with him if things got sticky. He finally caught the girl's eye and threw the full power of the male principle right at her. Suddenly he realized with surprise that she did not seem to be seeing him. She was looking right through him at someone in back of him. He did not seem to be able to get any response out of her . . .

It was several days before Dillon found out that he had been made the victim of an elaborate fraud.

The chemist's analysis showed that the green powder was nothing but green pastel crayon which had been ground up in a blender. The capsules came from the corner drug store and his beautiful sumptuously-dressed lady love of a few nights before had been a talented Broadway actress who played her part perfectly for $5,000. Frank had also paid the other girl, the amorous one in the bar and had tipped her off in advance that he wanted to play a practical joke on his friend.

Dillon's lawyers told him that the sales contract was so cleverly drawn that even if he could find Frank it would be exceedingly difficult to indict him for fraud. He had clearly disclaimed any guarantee concerning the pills or what they would do. In fact, he had actually stated in the sales contract that he thought the pills were worthless.

Frank played it safe, however. Perhaps he was afraid of the Federal income tax authorities. He was never seen again.

THE FUTURE THAT VANISHED

♠

A weird and terrible rumor was going around the very important and sophisticated city of Metropolis. It was about the city's social leader and her ravishingly beautiful niece. It seems that the social leader, whom we will call Mrs. Van Astorbilt, was interested in fortune tellers. In fact, she made it a principle never to make any important decision without first discussing it with her fortune teller.

She had a beautiful niece, Janet, whom she had brought up from the South to present to society. The coming-out party Mrs. Van Astorbilt gave for her was the talk of the city. Janet turned out to be easily the most sensational debutante of the year. A highly amusing girl with a flare for getting along with people, she was one of those rare women, a raving beauty who would have made it on personality even if she had been ugly.

Mrs. Van Astorbilt, having no children of her own, lavished all of the instincts of her frustrated motherhood on her lovely niece. It was her ambition that she make a brilliant marriage. She even had a highly-classified secret list of eligible bachelors that she approved of and who

were always present at the succession of brilliant parties
she was constantly giving for her niece.

One day, to Mrs. Van Astorbilt's horror, she discovered something that threatened all her dreams for her
niece's future. Always a curious and nosy person who
could not bear not knowing everything, she was snooping
around her niece's desk when she came upon a note that
electrified her. "My lovely darling," it started. It was
written in a bold scrawl with a heavy pen and jet black
ink.

As Mrs. Van Astorbilt swiftly read the letter, her lips
parted in dismay. It didn't worry her that her niece was
obviously having a very heavy love affair. After all, that's
what beautiful women were made for. But what a man to
have it with. She remembered him now. It was bad
enough that he had no money and had gone to some
university out in the Middle West, but his family was
absolutely impossible.

Mrs. Van Astorbilt looked up with horrified eyes.
When a girl married a man, she also married his family.
In this case it would be like mixing oil and water. You
could stir like mad, she thought, but they always quickly
separated out again into layers.

Mrs. Van Astorbilt closed her eyes spasmodically.
Suddenly she had a splitting headache. What she needed
was a warm, perfumed bath. She had to think this matter
out thoroughly.

An hour later, submerged in her bath, Mrs. Van
Astorbilt knew that she did not have the courage to
confront her niece with her love affair. It would be impossible to admit that she had read the letter.

Suddenly Mrs. Van Astorbilt's eyes widened and she
sat bolt upright in the bathtub. The perfumed bubbles flew
in all directions and slopped onto the floor. She would take
Janet down to her fortune teller. She could tip Madam
Amuranth off in advance about the love affair and even

give her the boy's name. Janet had inherited more than a little of her own superstitious nature. And, Mrs. Van Astorbilt thought with satisfaction, that piece of information coming from a fortune teller with a pack of cards would shock the bejesus out of her.

Mrs. Van Astorbilt got out of the tub and started drying herself. For most women, life was a bitch in heat. You always had to keep thinking of unusual things if you were to keep on top of the business of being a woman, and that's exactly what she was doing. She would just get her fortune teller to tell Janet that such a marriage would never do. Scare the pants right off of Janet and that would be that. She would take her down to Madam Melahat Amuranth tomorrow "just for a lark." And that, by God, would be the end of that.

The next day Mrs. Van Astorbilt unfolded her plan to Madam Amuranth. The black gypsy eyes of the fortune teller bored into her own. Her swift oriental mind was counting up the chips like a calculator. Exactly what was Mrs. Van Astorbilt getting at? Was she testing her to see if she was really a fraud? Couldn't risk anything like that. When your best customer was involved you had to play it close to the chest. "Mrs. Van Astorbilt," she finally said, "I have always been almost religiously careful to let no element of fraud touch my gift for prophecy because I regard it as a trust. Sometimes it has been a temptation. There have been times when I have found out facts about certain of my clients I could have startled them with by saying they came out of my cards. I have always resisted such temptations because many people think the art of prophecy is a fraud anyway, without having it actually turn into one."

Madam Amuranth paused. "There are few things, though, that a person will not do for friendship. And I know, of course, that this could turn into the most serious problem of your life. Bring your niece in here tomorrow afternoon and I will tell her all about her love affair and try to shock her right out of it. I will start in with both of you right in the room. I will tell your niece's fortune from the cards. Then suddenly I will tell her I have something of so private a nature that I must talk to her alone."

"Very subtle, indeed."

The next day Janet and her aunt were in Madam Amuranth's "salon." Janet's eyes were glowing with anticipation. "I've heard so much about you from my aunt," she said. "It is incredible what you do and how easily you do it."

Madam Amuranth smiled. "A gift is always mysterious to everyone except the person who has it. I would much rather be a writer or an actress. This just happens to be the gift I have. You certainly can't make much money by predicting people's futures."

Madam Amuranth sat Janet down at the table opposite her and started to deal out a pack of cards face up on the table. Slowly, as Janet and Mrs. Van Astorbilt watched her in fascination, she dealt out about fifteen cards. Suddenly she stopped and the color left her face. Suddenly she looked up at them with a stricken look.

"Something has happened here on the table," she said, "that has never happened before in my life of predicting the future." She paused. "If the next card is the king of spades, it will be impossible for me to continue telling your fortune."

The two women looked at her, outraged. Mrs. Van Astorbilt's nose went up in the air. "I have already hired you to tell my niece's fortune," she said stiffly, "and you have accepted the job."

Madam Amuranth acted as though she had not heard. She reached slowly and turned over the top card. It was the king of spades. She slowly put the card down on the table and her face turned red with embarrassment. "I am sorry," she stammered, "but I cannot go on."

Mrs. Van Astorbilt glared at the fortune teller. "What do you mean you are not going to go on?"

Madam Amuranth's black eyes were pools of misery. "I—I don't dare go on," she stammered. "My profession has a code of ethics like every other profession. All I can tell you is that I cannot go on." She shook her head at the two startled women. "You will have to be satisfied with one thing," she turned to Mrs. Van Astorbilt, "and let me tell you, there will be no charge for this at all."

Mrs. Van Astorbilt's voice was sharp. "What thing will you do?"

"I will write your niece's fortune out on a piece of paper and seal it in an envelope. I will only do this, though, if you each give me your word of honor that you will not open the envelope until tomorrow morning."

Janet smiled. "Is this some sort of a practical joke, or something?"

"I only wish that it were," Madam Amuranth said. "Predicting the future is not always pleasant for the prophet. I would much rather not write it out but, because of my long relationship with Mrs. Van Astorbilt, I will, if you each give me your word of honor that under no circumstances will you open it before tomorrow morning."

After getting their promises Madam Amuranth went to another table. She scribbled for a moment on a piece of paper, put it into an envelope and sealed it up. She handed the letter to Mrs. Van Astorbilt. "I am sorry I cannot continue today. You will see why, though, soon enough."

On the way home Mrs. Van Astorbilt's chauffeur, a retainer who had been with her for twenty years, had a heart attack. He flopped forward over the steering wheel and the heavy automobile swerved into the opposing line of traffic. There was a stunning crash and Mrs. Van Astorbilt's last memory was of flying through the air.

When Mrs. Van Astorbilt woke up in the hospital and

found that both her niece and her chauffeur had been killed, she immediately became hysterical. She did not remember anything for a few days and her friends who came to see her were understandably worried.

Suddenly, on the morning of the third day, it was as if a switch had been turned off. Her hysterics disappeared completely and she stared horrified at her nurse. "Get me my handbag," she said. The startled nurse picked it up from the dresser and handed it to her. Mrs. Van Astorbilt was mumbling to herself. "My niece's future," she muttered. She took the fortune teller's letter out of her bag and opened it. "Janet's future," she muttered again as she opened the envelope and unfolded the letter. The cleanly inscribed words written by Madam Amuranth for her niece screamed up at her from the paper.

"You have no future."

The weird story spread like wildfire and everyone who came to the hospital to see Mrs. Van Astorbilt stared at the letter. Everyone was aghast at the frightful accuracy of Madam Amuranth's prophecy. The next thing most of them did was to rush over to the obviously exasperated Madam Amuranth to have their own fortunes told. Any questions they asked about Janet or Mrs. Van Astorbilt were always answered with a stiff silence. "I never, under any circumstances, discuss my clients' affairs with anyone."

And then the rush really started. Madam Amuranth was absolutely swamped. She doubled her fees and the number of her clients only increased faster. Finally, in desperation she made them three times higher than they were before, but her clientele only increased the faster. As the story of her ghastly prophecy spread, people even flew in from other parts of the country to consult her. She swiftly became wealthy and fat.

When Mrs. Van Astorbilt got out of the hospital, she ordered her niece's room to be left exactly the way it was at the moment when they had left for the fortune teller's. In another frame, under a famous painting which had been done of Janet by Eileen Ingalls, there was the piece of paper with the words written in the fortune teller's neat calligraphy.

"YOU HAVE NO FUTURE"

The real story did not come out for years. It then turned out that the whole episode was an elaborate fraud. Although even her closest friends did not know it, Mrs. Van Astorbilt was in desperate need of money. She could have lived comfortably on her income but that would have been tantamount to death. She had to have her chauffeur, her expensive car, her parties, her clubs and her luxuries. The question of finances was one of the principal problems which she usually discussed in her sessions with Madam Amuranth.

The day after the automobile wreck had killed Janet, Madam Amuranth came to visit Mrs. Van Astorbilt at the hospital. "I know, Mrs. Van Astorbilt, that this is not the time to talk about anything important. Unfortunately right now is the only time it can ever be talked about. I spread out my cards last night and told your fortune. They showed clearly that you are about to come into a continuing income which will last as long as you live."

"How is that possible? I have no living relatives that can leave me any money, and I cannot very well work for a living myself."

"My cards never lie. And in this case I have the proof in my own hands."

"What do you mean by that?"

"I mean that you can make a decision within the next ten minutes that will solve all of your financial problems for the predictable future. In ten minutes, though, the opportunity will vanish forever."

"How absolutely extraordinary! What is it?"

"There are certain facts that have to be admitted. Your niece is dead and your chauffeur is dead. My ability to tell the future is a genuine gift."

"There is no question about any of those facts."

"Unfortunately, very few people know about the last one. If something dramatic could happen to show everyone that I have this priceless gift, the amount of money I would then make would be much more than enough for both of us."

Mrs. Van Astorbilt sat bolt upright in bed. "Exactly what are you driving at?"

"If you could do something to greatly increase my income, I would be delighted to give you half of it. I have thought of a way that, with your help, I could make four or five thousand dollars a month. I would give you half of it."

The pain in Mrs. Van Astorbilt's head vanished in a twinkling. "Two thousand dollars a month for me? What do I have to do, murder someone?"

Madam Amuranth laughed. "It's much less drastic than that." She paused. "Why not tell everyone that you brought your niece to see me about a love affair just before your accident? You could say that after one look at the cards I burst into tears and refused to tell Janet her fortune. You insisted that I tell it, though, and I finally compromised by sealing it up in an envelope to be looked at the next day. After your accident and her death, you opened the envelope and my prophecy for her was, *YOU HAVE NO FUTURE.*"

Mrs. Van Astorbilt looked at Madam Amuranth with a stunned look on her face. "Two thousand dollars a month," she mumbled.

"I have brought a pad of paper, a pen, and an envelope. I can write the note out right here for you and put it in your bag. If you recover your memory tomorrow, open my letter and tell everyone about it, and show it around, my cards tell me that the financial problems of both of us will be completely solved."

Once the weird story started circulating, the income that came in was beyond their wildest expectations. It went on for many years until Madam Amuranth's unexpected and unpredicted death of pneumonia.

ISTANBUL LAWSUIT

♠

Prior to the massive social reforms brought in by Turkey's great statesman Mustapha Kemal Ataturk, the Turkish legal and judicial systems operated on the same venal basis many of the nation's other institutions did. The impossibility involved in trying to run a nation which was attempting to modernize and industrialize by use of the old Koranic legal system was further complicated by the corruption of the courts themselves.

Ataturk changed all this by setting up a research project designed to find the world's most workable legal system. His theory was to find it and then copy it for his native land.

After a thorough investigation most of his experts seemed to feel that the world's best criminal code was that of the Italians and the best civil code was the one developed by the Swiss.

With characteristic speed and energy, Ataturk decided to adopt both codes, each in its field, and he swiftly made this the law of the land.

The difficulties attendant on having such a code

which stemmed basically from two different sources, and which perforce had to be interpreted by the old Koranic judges in the light of their Koranic background, were formidable indeed. During the inevitable shakedown period, the main argument of its proponents was that, clumsy as it might appear in the initial stages, it was infinitely better than the old system which Ataturk had replaced. The "New Turks" who backed Ataturk were fond of supporting their point with the story of an American tourist's experience with the old system.

One Lysander Morris (name fictitious), who had majored in Middle Eastern languages at college, was taking the grand tour of the area with his wife. It was back in the confused days before the Ataturk Revolution. Morris spoke fluent Turkish, so Turkey was particularly fascinating to him.

Collectors of sorts, Morris and his wife were wandering through the Istanbul Bazaar, the huge, covered area which used to house the Sultan's horses, when suddenly he stopped dead in his tracks. In the window of one of the tiny shops in the covered Bazaar was what looked like a genuine old Rhodes platter. If he was right, it could have been anywhere between five hundred and a thousand years old. Whispering to his wife to look nonchalant and disinterested, Morris wandered aimlessly around the little shop picking up and pricing various objects. Finally, as if by happenstance, they came to the platter. "How much is this?" he asked. The Bazaar keeper smiled ingratiatingly. "For you, sir, and only because you are my first customer of the morning, the platter will be two thousand lire."

The American put down the platter as if it was red hot. "Too much for me," he said. He stood thinking. Two thousand lire. *Christmas*, that was a lot of money. It was really worth about a thousand lire.

"Where are you staying, effendi?"

"At the Park Hotel in Hayas Pasa."

"Will you be here long?"

"About a week."

"Why don't you take the platter back to your hotel and look at it? See if it grows on you. If you don't like it, bring it back. If you do like it, we can probably argue out some price that is satisfactory."

That night the American stared at the platter as it stood on its stand on his dresser. There was certainly no doubt about its being genuine. The trouble was that the Bazaar keeper had set too high a price on it—by just about a hundred percent. He sat and admired the beautiful lateen-rigged ship sailing across the platter with its breathtaking colors, and the porpoises frolicking in the green water. He just had to have it, he decided, as he turned off the light.

Morris was awakened that night by a loud crashing and banging at his door. He stumbled out of bed and turned the knob. The door flew open, almost knocking him down. There were three police officers standing in the door. Behind them stood the Bazaar keeper from the shop where he had gotten the plate.

"That's the American, all right." It was the Bazaar keeper pointing at him. "The one who promised to pay me for the platter."

The biggest police officer looked at Morris aggressively. "Ali the Shopkeeper has filed a legal action against you. He said you took his platter, promising to pay him two thousand lira, and you have not paid the money. He is afraid you will get out of the country without paying him."

Morris was outraged. "*He* was the one who suggested that I take the platter," he shouted. "To see if I liked it. Here it is on the dresser. He can take his blasted plate. I don't want it." He handed the plate to Ali, who put his hands firmly behind his back.

"I want my two thousand lire," he said. "You have bought the platter and I want the money, not the platter."

The police officer looked at Morris arrogantly. "I am afraid," he said in perfect English, "we will have to take you off to jail."

Morris' hair practically stood on end. Turkish jails had a reputation that had even got back to the United States. A moment later he was talking to his only American friend in Istanbul, the representative of a large American tobacco company. The tobacco man's voice came thin and scratchy over the ancient telephone. "I'll get a good lawyer," he said, "and come right over."

At the trial a few days later, Ali the Shopkeeper's attorney got up and respectfully addressed the judge. "This American tourist," he said, "Mr. Lysander Morris, came into my client's shop in the covered Bazaar, admired the Rhodes platter, and asked its price. When told that its price was two thousand lire he said, 'I will buy it and take it with me and pay you later this afternoon. I have not got two thousand lire with me.' My client graciously assented to this, and Mr. Morris went back to his hotel with the platter. He has never paid my client the two thousand lire which he owes him."

Lysander Morris jumped to his feet. "It is a lie," he shouted. His lawyer, Mehmed Effendi, pulled him back down in his chair. "Keep quiet," he whispered. "Above all, you cannot be disrespectful to the judge. Wait, wait."

The judge graciously ignored Morris' outburst. "Have you," he asked of the opposing council, "any witnesses to this transaction?"

"We certainly have." He motioned to a middle-aged woman. "Get up, Byan Fawzia, and tell us what you saw." The woman, a veil covering the lower part of her face, cast her eyes modestly down at the floor. "I was standing in Ali the Shopkeeper's shop, when the American came in and picked up the dish. He inquired about its price and when Ali said two thousand lire, he said, 'I will buy it, but I will have to go back to my hotel to get the money.' He walked out with the dish in his hand."

Morris again tried to scramble to his feet. "There was no one in the store at all," he whispered firmly to his attorney. "Except my wife and me and the Shopkeeper."

His attorney pulled him back to his chair with a steely grip. "Keep quiet," he hissed, "or you will spoil everything."

To Morris' astonishment four more witnesses, none of whom he had ever seen before, swore that they were in the shop and had heard him agree to pay two thousand lire for the platter.

Crushed, Morris sat fuming in his chair as his lawyer took his turn on the stand.

"My client," he began, "did indeed come into the shop of Ali the Shopkeeper. But here, Your Honor, the stories begin to differ. Morris effendi picked up the platter and asked its price. Ali the Shopkeeper said, 'two thousand lire.' Mr. Morris said, 'Splendid. I will buy it—'"

Morris looked up, startled, at his attorney. Was he in on the crooked deal too? For Christ's sake—two thousand lire. He started to get to his feet. His attorney shot him a warning glance and he subsided.

"My client," the attorney continued, "said, 'splendid.' He then took two thousand lire out of his billfold and paid Ali the Shopkeeper for the platter and walked out of the shop with it."

Lysander Morris, too shocked to speak, sank back into his chair.

The judge looked steadily at Morris' lawyer. "But we have just heard four witnesses who said that no money was paid at all."

The lawyer bowed respectfully from the waist, "They lied, Your Honor," he said amiably. "The first one lied, also the second, the third, and the fourth. All lied. It is like our

ancient Turkish saying, 'Dead fish lying on the dock all point in the same direction.' "

The lawyer turned to a man sitting nearby.

Ibrahim, a tall, dignified Turk with a red fez, bowed respectfully to the judge. "I was standing in the shop, Your Honor, thinking to make a purchase, when the American came in and looked at the platter. He obviously liked it very much. 'How much is this?' he asked. 'Two thousand lire,' Ali answered. Then the American immediately paid him two thousand lire and walked out with his platter."

As Morris sat stunned in his chair, his lawyer brought up ten witnesses. Each one said he had seen him pay the two thousand lire for the platter.

The court held that Morris owned the platter and had already paid two thousand lire for it. Deafened by the indignant howls of the Bazaar keeper and his attorney, Morris stumbled, dazed, out of the courtroom holding the beautiful platter in his hand. He looked blankly at his lawyer. "That," he said, "was the goddamnedest thing I have ever seen in my life. What is your fee for handling a case like that?"

The lawyer looked apologetic, "I had a little trouble lining up the witnesses," he admitted. "The whole bill, including my services, will come to one thousand lire."

Morris smiled for the first time in two days. "That makes me feel a helluva lot better," he said. "That is the exact price I was willing to pay for the platter."

THE HAUNTED HOUSE

♠

As Melahat came into the room, her three friends looked at her with quick sympathy. Her eyes were tired and she did not appear to have her usual bounce. Florence James was particularly solicitous. "I can see you had it again," she said. There was a slight question in her voice.

Melahat took off her coat. "I certainly did," she said in a puzzled tone of voice, "me, of all people, getting mixed up in something offbeat like this." She smiled. "After all, I am supposed to be an expert in things that verge on the supernatural."

Joan Fletcher took Melahat's coat and laid it over a chair. "Was it exactly the same as the last time?"

Melahat shook her head resignedly. "Exactly, and if anything even more crystal clear. There is something very weird about it. Something I just don't understand. The psychiatrists tell us that dreams are something that boil up out of our subconscious. That they tend to balance out the frustrations of our lives, and that their real purpose is to keep us sane and mentally healthy." Melahat looked puzzled. "But why, then, would a healthy, happy, bal-

97

anced person like me keep having exactly the same dream over and over and over again? It's really beginning to worry me. It seems like a sappy thing, really, but I've decided to get the thing down on paper accurately enough so that I'll be able to check and see if it changes at all." She stood thinking. "Let's see now. It was three bridge games ago that I first told you about it. So this will be the fourth time I have had exactly the same queer dream."

Mabel Von Nostrand opened her purse and took out a pen and a piece of paper. "There's not the slightest use being a procrastinator," she said. "And we can hold up our bridge game a few minutes. You've probably forgotten that, thanks to Dad, I can take shorthand almost as fast as some secretaries. Now you just sit down, Melahat, and dictate it slowly, exactly the way you remember it. I'll type it up tonight and mail it to you."

Melahat sat down with obvious reluctance. "This is such a damn fool thing, really, I'm not enthusiastic about having too many people know about it. If you weren't three of my very best friends in the world I certainly wouldn't admit anything like this. It makes me sound as if I am ready for the rest home." She smiled brightly. "And at thirty-five I hope I'm a lot too young for that."

Mabel settled herself down at the table with her pen poised. "Now let's cut out the chit-chat," she said, "and just repeat your dream exactly as you remember it."

"Well—I dream that I am walking along a street of this very city. I don't recognize the street, but for some reason I know it is this city and I know it is the late afternoon. I have a sort of feeling that if I could ever find the street this whole thing would go away and I would be free of it. Anyway, I am walking along the street and I come to a part of the street where the houses are spaced far apart. They are about twenty feet above the street level and back maybe a hundred feet. In my dream I find myself standing on the sidewalk in front of one of these houses. For some reason I feel very strongly drawn to the house. I can't see it completely because it's back over the rise, but I can see the top two floors of it. It is a large brick house with white pillars in front, obviously a really old one, over a hundred years old, and extremely attractive-looking. It looks as if it was made by one of those wonderful old colonial architects." Melahat smiled. "In fact, it's just the kind of house I've always wanted," she hesitated, "my dream house."

Joan Fletcher was looking at her friend with parted lips. "How spooky," she said.

"It sure is. There is always a flight of terrazzo steps that curve up from the sidewalk level. They curve around to the left and end up in the little brick walk that goes to the front door of the house."

Melahat looked slightly embarrassed. "For some queer reason, I am so attracted to the house that I always start climbing the stairs. And there I get one of the few clues I have as to where the house is. As I come up the stairs, I see that the sun is setting slightly to the left of the house, which means, of course, because it's late afternoon, that it's on the west side of the street."

Melahat looked determined. "At least that cuts off seventy-five percent of the work if I ever decide I have to find this house. Maybe I should drive up and down all the north and south streets in our city just looking at the houses on the west side until I find it."

Florence James looked doubtful. "It would take you forever. There are thousands of miles of streets in Metropolis."

"Well, anyway, in my dream I climb the steps, and I've even counted their number. There are twenty-five steps that lead up to the brick sidewalk. When I finally get up there on the level of the house it absolutely fascinates me. I decide that I absolutely must own it, no matter what happens, I've *got* to own it or die. It's the house I've been subconsciously wanting for years. Everything about it is attractive. The old weathered bricks in the walk have grass growing up through their intersections. And there is a lovely old bronze sundial about fifteen feet to the left with its own little brick walk going right out to it. I always go out and look at it. Its shadow is always pointing at exactly the same time. Six o'clock." For a second Melahat's face looked frightened. "And it has a really spooky inscription on its face, 'Dreams are the things that life is made of.' "

A collective gasp went around the room. "How really spooky."

"That happens every single time?"

"What a queer dream."

"Now you can see why I look so bedraggled. Of course the last thing I do in my dream is exactly what any of you would do. I march straight up to the door and look for the bell, but there isn't any. There is only one of those old bronze bell pulls that they used to have in the old colonial mansions. In my dream I pull it and there is a sharp clang from way back inside the house."

Melahat paused. "A minute later the door slowly opens. A hideous-looking old woman is there standing in the door staring at me. I am frightened to death but I always say the same thing, 'This is a beautiful, lovely, old house and I've often admired it and wondered who lived here.' "

Melahat's face had become ashen. "And this is the part that for some reason I just can't bear to think about. A frightened, horrified look comes over the old woman's face, and every single time she does the same thing. She slams the door right in my face. It is then that I find myself with my eyes wide open lying in bed. I lie there trembling and unable to sleep for the rest of the night."

A murmur of sympathy went around the table. "How fantastic."

"Unbelievable."

Mabel Von Nostrand put the top back on her fountain pen. "I'll drop this off at your house tomorrow."

Suddenly Melahat's expression changed completely. "I'm not going to sit here like a damned ninny and smash up our weekly bridge game with a lot of sympathetic drivel about me. Tonight is the night we are going out to that marvelous new French restaurant, the Café Henri Secherez. It's supposed to have the best food in the city and its specialty, Mussels Maragnaire, is already getting a national reputation." Melahat picked up a pack of cards and started shuffling them. "Not one more word about my troubles, except this: they say that lucky in cards, unlucky in life. So this afternoon you better each keep a sharp eye on your pocketbooks."

Three hours later the bridge game ended. Joan Fletcher added up the score. "Melahat," she said, "you didn't win after all. You lost five dollars. Under your theory that means you are going to be lucky in life again. I'll bet you never have this queer dream again."

A few minutes later the four of them were in Melahat's automobile. Melahat turned to Joan Fletcher. "Tell Pierre where your Café Henri Secherez is; it sounds wonderful." The chauffeur put the car into gear and they went off, chattering like magpies about their mistakes in the bridge game they had just finished.

They had been driving about twenty minutes and were nearing the outskirts of Metropolis when Melahat suddenly let out a faint scream. "Stop, Pierre! Stop! Stop!" she said. Her voice was choked with emotion. Her friends looked at her with startled eyes. Mabel put her hand on her arm. "Is there something wrong, Melahat?"

"No. Something is just exactly right." She pointed with a trembling hand to their left across the street. "It's my house," she whispered. "The same house I keep seeing in my dreams. The exact same house."

The four women and the chauffeur stared across the street with wide-eyed astonishment. A curving flight of terrazzo stairs went up the twenty-five foot rise and disappeared over the brow of the hill. They could see part of the house peering over the hill, enough to see that it was made of red brick and had white pillars in front.

Melahat got out of the car without a word and started to march across the street. Her worried friends piled out after her. She started up the terrazzo stairs.

Mabel Von Nostrand opened her bag and took out her notes. At the top of the stairs she turned to the others. "There *are* just twenty-five steps," she said, in an awe-struck voice.

They hurried after Melahat, who was marching determinedly along the brick walk. They pointed silently at the green blades of grass coming up between the bricks and at the sundial, exactly where she had described it, a few feet off to one side. Florence stepped over to look at it and stared open-mouthed. She beckoned to the others. The shadow of the sundial was pointing exactly toward six o'clock. They gazed, speechless, at the ancient bronze inscription, "Dreams are the things that life is made of." And then they saw the sun, a round globe hanging in the sky. It was setting just to the left of the house.

Melahat was walking along the path like an automaton. Her eyes were slightly glazed and she shrugged off her friends as they hurried after her. There was no doorbell, but the bronze knob of the door pull she had dreamed about was right there beside the door. She stood for a moment with a frightened look on her face and then she pulled it. There was a melodious clang from way back inside the house. The four women waited tensely before the door.

Slowly the door opened and an evil-looking old woman appeared in the doorway. As she saw Melahat a look of horror came over her face.

"Please, please, don't slam the door. Please." There was desperation in Melahat's voice. "I want to buy this house. Please tell me who it belongs to."

For the first time the old lady spoke. "You would not want to own it," she said flatly.

"Why?"

"Because it is haunted."

Melahat's voice was a whisper. "Haunted? By whom?"

The look of horror in the old lady's face deepened. "Haunted—by you," she said, and slammed the door.

Melahat slumped down in a dead faint and her friends clustered around her. They lifted her up and half carried her back to the car. "I can't go on to the restaurant," she gasped. "Pierre, drop me off at home and then take my friends out to the Café Secherez."

The next day, to the astonishment of her friends, Melahat went to a real estate agent and found that the beautiful mansion had been empty for ten years and had been for sale the whole time. She bought it, repaired and refurnished it, and moved in.

A month later the members of the bridge club found Melahat radiant and healthy again. She looked ten years younger and was her old vivacious self. When she lost $20 in the bridge game her eyes sparkled with delight. "That only proves," she said, "that now I am lucky in life and unlucky in cards."

Melahat, of course, was our friend of two stories ago—Madam Amuranth, and this all happened in her salad days when she was the great fortune teller of Metropolis. This whole wild story was just another one of her many ways of publicizing her extraordinarily profitable fortune-telling business. In a few days her friends at the bridge table had retailed the story all over the city and it even appeared in the gossip columns.

Absolutely swamped with business, Melahat again

raised her already astronomical fees to cut down the crowds that were trooping up the twenty-five terrazzo stairs to her new home. There was something psychic about her, everyone agreed, and her new home seemed to focus and emphasize it. It was only another proof, after all, that things were not exactly what they seemed, and that the supernatural, and Madam Amuranth, were forces to be reckoned with.

It had all started when Melahat had decided she needed a new home. She picked out the "haunted house" as ideal for her purpose and, in fact, had actually purchased it long before the famous bridge game. Always sensitive to anything that might increase her fortune-telling business, she made up the story of her recurring dream and installed her chauffeur's old mother in the house, all ready to receive her and her guests on that dramatic day. She had even taken the trouble to have the old sundial installed in the yard. Its eerie inscription, "Dreams are the things that life is made of," was the touch that caught the public fancy, and everyone in the city wanted to see it. She had, of course, picked the Café Secherez and got Joan Fletcher to find out where it was because she already knew that the route to the café passed right by her new home.

THE DEADLY FRAUD AT AREA G

♠

It was World War II and General Nathaniel Irons, Regular Army, Retired, was sitting in his sumptuous office at Area G, outside Washington. He looked around him with satisfaction. Spies weren't too bad, really, when you got used to them. Quite a bit different from the regular Army types he had spent most of his life with, but the differences weren't all bad either. Being the commandant of a spy training camp told you one thing and that was the average spy had a subtle kind of angled way of looking at things that sometimes made you sit up in your chair. It was that they were trained for a different sort of survival than the Army was trained for. They put a lot of emphasis on going it alone and thinking fast, and being individually dangerous. Sometimes it made things quite unpredictable.

The General put his feet up on his desk. He certainly had nothing to complain about. Almost six years over retirement age and here he was having even more fun than he had had in World War I. It all boiled down to the fact that the spy service boys needed some old-fashioned Army brains around to steady them a little bit. Good old Army discipline had a place even in the spy war.

105

The General grinned, and he was still enough of a
kid to enjoy it. Calling his superior, the spy master, D, as
if he were a queer type of airplane or cannon was sort of
fun. D probably stood for death. He certainly had to admit
one thing, and that was the spies they were graduating
were killing a hell of a lot more than their weight in
enemy. That is, they were as long as their weight lasted. A
human life wasn't worth a good old-fashioned piss in the
bucket to these characters.

The General looked at his watch. D would be out any
minute now to see how his new "deflation" system worked.
D was putting a lot of trust in him and it all went back to
that original idea he had of having a Haunted House: a
house full of electronic gadgets that would precisely test a
spy's skill with his weapons, dummies lunging out of
closets with guns in their hands, trap doors opening up,
moving targets to shoot at. After the spy had followed that
little red line through all the rooms and out the back door
he could assign a definite mark for him in "weapons
facility." It was just like a college entrance examination.

The General looked impatiently at the door. D had
been delighted with the idea until the records started
coming in from the field. The records showed that the
higher the spy ranked in "weapons facility" in the
Haunted House Test, the quicker he got himself killed
when he got behind the enemy lines. It looked for a while
as though it would have been better not to train the sons
of bitches at all. Just give them a buggy whip and drop
them behind the lines.

The General looked at his watch again. D had solved
that one fast. The higher the mark you give a spy, the
more overconfident he gets. Even a drunken steeplejack
has more chance of survival than an overconfident spy.
Any spy who thinks his weapons are going to keep him
alive if he gets uncovered just doesn't last over the week-
end in the spy business. You can't fight a whole nation

behind its own lines just because you got an A in "weapons facility." D had looked at him with those frosty blue eyes. "General Irons," he had said, "put in a special test at the end of your training course that *absolutely everyone* will fail. A test of some kind that will badly humiliate them. Then chew the hell out of them for their stupid overconfidence."

General Irons smiled reminiscently. His first attempt had been such a flat failure that it had humiliated him instead of the students. His idea of dropping them out in the Blue Ridge wilderness below Washington with some phony maps that had gradually graded off into Outer Mongolia had sounded good. The General's smile broadened. It didn't fool the smart ones a bit. Two of them actually beat him back to Area G. These graduate counter-spies were acid sharp—no doubt about that. He did the same thing with a bunch of regular Army privates as a control. After two days they had to send out searching parties for them.

There was a knock on the door and D came into the room. He was a tall, heavy man with a huge, aquiline, nose.

"Good evening, General," he said gravely. "It's getting pretty dark out there and I don't want to miss this new ego-destroying test of yours. You'd better brief me a little before we start."

"We've tried to keep it simple. Everyone's last assignment in the weapons course is to sneak out at night and steal some weapons from our new weapons depot."

"Is that the one on the hill with the man-proof fence around it?"

"Yes, the one that is floodlighted for three hundred yards around. There is a guard standing inside the fence with a Tommy gun."

"How the hell can anyone do that? What weapon do you give them for the project?"

"Only their Black Fairburne fighting knife."

D chuckled. "I can't think of anything any more impossible than that, unless it's flying to the moon on a window blind."

"We hoke it up quite a bit to give it greater impact. As soon as our overconfident embryo spy appears in the floodlights the soldier behind the barbed wire fires his Tommy gun over his head and practically scares him to death. Then he brings him in to me with his hands high over his head, goosing him along with his gun."

"And then what happens?"

"I chew him out until he hasn't got enough ego left to blow the hat off a mosquito." The General smiled. "My son has been out at the block house for the last four nights with his Tommy gun. He volunteered in the regular Army and then asked for a transfer to us. I thought this might help break him in on our thinking. He has done his job well and is pretty excited about it. If he shows any aptitude I'd like to put him up before your screening board."

"Fine."

There was a knock on the door and a powerful-looking young man about six feet tall came into the room and saluted. He had a keen, intelligent face and the desperate, focused eyes of a fanatic.

"Daniel Delecroix reporting for his last test, Sir."

The General looked him up and down and turned to D. "This is the man who made such a high record in the Haunted House Test. In fact, he made the only perfect score that has ever been made in that test."

He turned to the young man. "What is the basis of our system here at Area G?" he barked.

"To obey orders swiftly and efficiently even if you do not know the reason for them."

"Why is that important?"

"The reason may be classified."

"What example did I give you to illustrate this?"

A faint smile appeared on the young man's face. "The General told us that if he ordered us to shoot an old lady in a wheel chair, shoot her immediately because it might be Hitler in disguise."

D grinned appreciatively.

"One more question. What does an order include?"

"An order includes any action that has to be performed in order to carry out the order."

The General permitted himself a grim smile. "Very good. I am now ordering you to go up and steal some weapons from the weapons depot on the hill. Are you armed?"

"Yes, Sir." The man produced a Smith and Wesson 357 Magnum from the shoulder holster under his arm.

The General took it. "Anything else?"

"Only a few assassination sticks." He handed the General a handful of small, deadly looking copper tubes.

The General handed the candidate a black steel knife with a triangular blue blade about eight inches long. "This is your only weapon for your project. We will wait here until you get back."

The man saluted smartly and left.

D looked at the General with warm approval. "I want to congratulate you, Nathaniel, on the way you're firming our people up out here. There are few things more formidable in a secret agent than the proper combination of discipline and ability to use individual initiative. How long does it usually take before your son marches our victim in at the point of a gun?"

"Usually about fifteen minutes."

A half an hour later the two men were looking at each other questioningly.

D chuckled. "Maybe your young man couldn't even find the weapons depot?"

"No, he's too smart for that. My son will be goosing him in here directly."

Ten minutes later there was a knock on the door and Delecroix stepped into the room. He was so loaded down with equipment he could hardly walk. Five Garand rifles were hanging from his neck by their slings. He was holding a bundle of four Tommy guns and a parachute carbine in his arms like a load of wood. A .45 automatic stuck out of one coat pocket and the other appeared to contain two hand grenades.

The General sprang to his feet. "Where in hell did you find all that stuff?" he barked.

"You ordered me to get some weapons from the weapons depot, Sir, and this was all I could carry."

The General felt a sickness in the pit of his stomach.

"What happened out there?"

"I went up to the edge of the floodlighted zone, Sir, and saw a man standing inside the man-proof fence with a Tommy gun. I remembered that speech you—I mean the General—always gave us. 'When something looks hard, don't blunder in like a fool and get your ass shot off. Sit down and think up a reasonable course of action.' "

"So what, exactly, did you do?"

"I went into the woods and sat down on a stump and worked out a plan. Then I came out into the floodlighted zone waving my handkerchief up over my head on a stick. The soldier behind the fence fired his Tommy gun over my head and almost scared me to death. I kept waving the flag, though, and finally I yelled up at him, 'Have any of the students I've sent come up there yet?' The soldier yelled back that they hadn't arrived yet. I yelled back that I wanted to come up and see how he handled them when they did arrive at the weapons depot."

The General stared at Delecroix with anguished eyes. "What did my son—what did the soldier do then?"

"The soldier behind the barbed wire took out his key

and opened up the gate in the fence, Sir, and let me in. He looked like an extremely nice fellow and I hated to do what my orders required."

The General's voice was harsh. "What did your orders require?"

"He still had his Tommy gun, Sir, so I waited until he turned his back and then plunged my knife into that spot above his right shoulder where you have shown us you can instantly kill a man. It certainly works, Sir. He is lying dead inside the man-proof fence."

PREDICTIONS OF THINGS TO COME

♠

Marmaduke Smith sat glumly in back of his fifteenth century desk and looked at his secretary, Donna Graham. There was just one piece of paper on the polished mahogany surface, a letter. His secretary looked acutely uncomfortable. "I know it's ridiculous—" she said.

"Of course it's ridiculous. Paying attention to an anonymous letter is always ridiculous."

"But Consolidated Electronics has already gone from 10 to 20 and the letter came in only the day before yesterday."

The industrialist had an exasperated look on his face. "You feel, do you, Donna, that whenever an anonymous letter comes in inviting me to buy some stock, I should fall all over myself to buy it without even knowing who sent the letter?"

"That does seem sort of silly," his secretary admitted, "but the stock has gone up almost—"

"I know it has," Smith said testily, "but there are just two ways it could possibly go and it might just as well have gone down as up." He picked up the letter and started to read it.

112

Dear Mr. Smith:

Please do not lose this letter, as it may turn out to be of considerable monetary value to you in the not too distant future. I am a little embarrassed writing it because it will be the first anonymous letter I have ever written, but as I intend to reveal my identity to you in the near future, it is only quasi-anonymous. I am withholding my identity now only because the early stages of the plan I am carrying out may appear to be foolish, and, for the moment, I do not wish to be contacted and subjected to humiliation.

In the next few weeks I am going to send you a number of prophecies about entirely different subjects. Each one will be concerning a subject on which no one could possibly make a logical prediction. Each one of these prophecies will turn out to be one hundred per cent correct. After they have turned out to be correct I will disclose my identity to you, and reveal my system.

My first prophecy will be as follows:

The price of the common shares of Consolidated Electronics, a corporation listed on the Stock Exchange, will more than double in value in the next few days.

I hasten to point out that I am not running a stock market touting service and this will probably be the last of my prophecies that has anything to do with the stock market. They will be about a variety of different subjects that have no connection with each other at all.

Very truly yours,
E.S.P.

Marmaduke Smith looked up from the letter. "Arrant nonsense," he said, and sailed it across the desk. "Imagine anyone calling himself E.S.P."

Miss Graham picked up the letter. "That's short for extra-sensory perception. I was intrigued by this letter when it came in," she admitted. "Also, I have a funny, queer, weird feeling about it. My woman's intuition or something. Just on an impulse I bought a hundred shares of Consolidated Electronics for $1000. And now it's worth $2000."

Marmaduke Smith looked at her with astonishment. "What if it had gone down 10 points?" he demanded.

"I would have lost my money."

Four days later, Miss Graham's eyes were sparkling with excitement. "Another letter from the same person," she said, "the man who predicted that Consolidated Electronics would go up."

"How do you know it's the same person?"

"Because he enclosed a carbon of his first letter with this one."

"What's his prediction this time?"

"He says that Pat McGuire is going to upset the Mayor and win the election next week."

"That would certainly be a hell of a note. Luckily, it's not very likely."

"He also says," she started reading the letter, " 'you now have an enormous profit in Consolidated Electronics. I now predict that it is going to go down so you had better sell it at the market.' "

"Have you still got your stock?"

Donna looked slightly flustered. "No, I just sold it 5 minutes ago." She hesitated. "And then I sold another hundred shares short." She looked smugly at Smith. "So far I've tripled my money," she said.

The morning after the election, Marmaduke Smith found Miss Graham standing in front of his desk with a queer look on her face.

"Another letter from E.S.P.," she said.

Marmaduke Smith glanced impatiently at the letter.

"With all the different top-drawer responsibilities I've got, you think I should be wasting my time reading trash like this?"

"But, Mr. Smith, he was absolutely right on the election, too. And he was also absolutely right on Consolidated Electronics' going down. I've made almost $5000 out of a $1000 investment."

Mr. Smith took the letter with a resigned look on his face and started to read it.

Dear Mr. Smith:

I assume that you have multiplied your investment by five times, at least, on Consolidated Electronics. If you rode it down on the short side as I, of course, assumed you would, I think it is now time to cover your short interest. I'm not predicting that it will go up but it is just that I don't know what the future is in regard to this stock. Uncertainty about the future always makes me uneasy.

Although the results will not be out until tomorrow (after this letter is mailed) you will have found out by this time that I was also right about the mayoralty election. I assume that after getting my prediction, a man of your financial importance and political sophistication hedged yourself by giving a contribution to McGuire in order to obligate him to you.

The look of exasperation on Marmaduke Smith's face deepened as he continued reading.

My next prediction is that the month-end statement by Poors and Moody Financial Service of freight car loadings in the New York City area will end with an odd rather than an even number.

Very truly yours,
E.S.P.

Marmaduke Smith looked up at his secretary. "How in the hell can anyone predict the last number on freight car loadings? The individual actions of millions of people all over the world, some starting months and even years ago, all have an effect on the freight car loadings in New York City. This fellow is a crackpot."

"But he has predicted everything else right."

"But even a stopped clock is right twice a day."

"But he has been right three times."

Four days later Marmaduke Smith looked at his secretary with a trace of uncertainty in his eyes. "That son of a bitch was right about the freight car loadings too," he said.

Miss Graham smiled. "That doesn't surprise me one bit. My Lebanese roommate says the Arabs have a proverb, 'What has been, will be.' A person can think up all sorts of excuses and reasons for each of these predictions but the most important thing is that they have *all* been right, *every single one.*" Miss Graham leaned across the desk. "And here is his letter for today."

"What does he predict?"

"He makes a prediction on the world's championship boxing match that you are going to see next Thursday at Madison Square Garden. He says McGurk will win."

"Hell, I've already made a fairly big bet on Pignatelli."

Miss Graham looked smug. "You had better hedge that bet. I just laid down five hundred dollars on McGurk."

Mr. Smith looked at his secretary with puzzled amusement. "Maybe you're right. Call my betting broker and put five thousand dollars on McGurk."

The next Friday there was another letter from E.S.P. It contained carbons of each of his previous letters.

Dear Mr. Smith:

As you can see, my prediction, as usual, was correct and McGurk knocked out Pignatelli in the sixth round. I hope you made as much money betting on the match as I did.

If you are not convinced by now that I have developed a method of predicting certain future situations you will never be convinced and this is the last letter you will ever receive from me.

If, on the other hand, my predictions interest you, please write me a letter stating a date and time when I can come to your office and see you. Send the letter to ESP, Box 4326 A, Post Office, New York. As soon as I get your note I will confirm the appointment by telephone.

Very truly yours,
E.S.P.

When E.S.P. came into the office, both Marmaduke Smith and his secretary were stunned with surprise. They had both expected something wild and unusual looking. E.S.P. was tall and lean. He was faultlessly and very conservatively dressed and looked like someone you would see at a British Embassy party. He even carried an umbrella and a thin, dark-colored attaché case. He had a direct and completely no-nonsense approach.

"Mr. Smith," he said, "you must be wondering about my anonymous letters. I assure you that I am not in character in sending out anonymous letters to people." He hesitated. "The fact is, Mr. Smith, I have stumbled onto something so unusual that the regular rules of communicating with people don't hold up very well. I've got to be extremely careful that people don't think I am a crazy crackpot. I am the Vice President of an old and extremely conservative establishment and I can't take any chance of having a purely personal matter, important as it is, adversely affect an organization I've spent a good part of my life in. In fact, I am going to have to ask your indulgence and continue to remain anonymous a while longer. My background is largely mathematical and scientific and if any of my associates knew that I was mixed up in something like this before I could prove it to them it might be disastrous."

Mr. Smith looked at his visitor suspiciously. "I might as well be frank with you Mr.—"

"For the moment just call me E.S.P."

"—Mr. E.S.P., and tell you that I'm not particularly enthusiastic about having a conversation with someone I can't identify. Just as frankly, though, I'm exceedingly curious as to how you do this trick. You made five very difficult prophecies, said you were going to hit all of them, and you did. Like the school kid watching the magician, I'd just like to know how you did it."

His visitor looked at Smith for a moment in silence. "I might as well be just as frank with you, Mr. Smith, as you have been with me. You will never know how I did it and neither will anyone else. That is my secret, and one that no one else is apt to uncover for a long, long time. I can, however, make the benefits of that secret available to you and that's what I am here now to do."

"Exactly what do you mean by that?"

"I first got interested in the subject of prophecy through reading of the researches of Dr. Rhine of Duke University on extra-sensory perception, precognition and thought-transference. Being of a scientific background, I was willing to have an open mind about things like E.S.P. and thought-transference, but only if they were proven by concrete experiments. Man is an electrical mechanism and, of course, electrical impulses and waves can be detected from a distance. When the firefly lights his light he is just sending out a train of electromagnetic vibrations which happen to be in the range of our eyes. Most of the electromagnetic spectrum is outside our visual range, but just because we don't see it doesn't mean it isn't there. Dr. Rhine's experiments with people looking at a special pack of cards in one room and having someone name the cards in another room a hundred feet away seemed to me to be remotely possible scientifically. Possibly a case similar to the firefly but involving the sending out of trains of invisible waves which were picked up, like radio waves, by some mechanism other than the eye."

Mr. Smith's visitor smiled wryly. "My scientific background, however, completely rejected Dr. Rhine's conclusions on what he called precognition. No matter how great the experimental evidence, I was unwilling to believe that a person could possibly know what throw of the dice was going to come up next." He paused. "Unless, of course, the dice were loaded."

Mr. E.S.P. paused again. "I am not going into the details of my own experimentation because I don't want anyone else baying off on the same trail. I eventually found out, though, that Dr. Rhine was completely right and that I and my scientific background were completely wrong about precognition.

"I found that under certain unusual conditions, if I put a really heavy mental effort on certain types of problems, my percentage of hits on a future prediction in some cases approached 100 per cent. My experiments didn't gear in, though, at all with Dr. Rhine's. Possibly I'm not a very good subject or haven't got exactly the right approach. I haven't been able to do it at all, for example, with things like dice or playing cards or roulette wheels." Mr. E.S.P. shook his head sadly. "If I had, I certainly wouldn't be here. I'd be making millions of dollars out in Las Vegas. I'm not exactly sure, but I think it's the presence of other people that confuses me so much that I get no results at all. I must be absolutely alone.

"I don't want to sound too quasi-scientific, but maybe everyone has these brain waves and currents, which he or she is sending out all the time. Maybe, to receive anything important, I've just got to be alone and away from all the other-person static."

Mr. Smith's visitor looked apologetic. "I'm afraid this is turning into a monologue and I don't want to sound like a complete ass. After all, our relationship is either going to terminate permanently in the next ten minutes or it is going to emerge into something enormously profitable to both of us. The fact of the matter is, Mr. Smith, that I can sometimes go off in a quiet place where there are no people near me and, in certain situations, I can sit down, concentrate my mind with an almost painful focus on one particular problem, and eventually come up with a pretty fair prediction in regard to it. I did that in the case of each prediction I sent to you: what stock was going to go up or down, who was going to win the race for Mayor, the boxing match and then the odd number at the end of the box car loadings. It requires a terribly unpleasant and really fearful mental concentration and I don't like to do it one little bit. If it can be made to pay off, though, it is going to be my main activity from now on."

Mr. E.S.P. opened his attaché case and took out a ledger. "After thinking of all sorts of ways I could profit from such a gift and, of course, I have purposely not told you exactly how I do it, it was obvious that there was just one way to cash in big and that was the stock market. I didn't want any of my friends to lose money so I took two thousand dollars out of savings and here is my record of purchases and sales for the last six months. My $2000 has grown to over $8500 and in not one single case have I been wrong on a stock's future movement. In each case I predicted when it would go up and in each case I was able to predict when to sell it."

Mr. Smith looked over the ledger with intense interest. It certainly didn't seem to be a fake. In fact he remembered one or two of the situations himself. "Who is your broker?" he asked.

Mr. E.S.P. smiled. "If I told you that, you could find out who I am. Part of any deal we would make would be that my anonymity would be completely respected until I wanted to disclose myself." Mr. E.S.P.'s voice suddenly became brusque. "But I've given you all the information I intend to, so we might as well either get down to business or terminate our conversation and let me go on to someone else. Frankly, it's pretty exasperating to me to be able to do this and have just a few thousand dollars to play with. While I was increasing two thousand dollars to eighty-five hundred a rich person might just as well have been increasing from two hundred thousand dollars to close to a million. And giving me twenty per cent of his profits. I never deal in cats and dogs so my choice will always be a stock that is registered on the Big Board. Also, I don't want to be handling any money myself. I want someone as an associate who will handle his own money through his own broker and keep me informed as to exactly how much he buys and sells, for how much and when. I am looking for the sort of person who can keep his mouth tightly shut so everyone else won't be in on our profit and who will pay me twenty per cent of his winnings in cash the day he sells his securities."

"How about losses?"

"There are going to be no more losses in the future than there have been in the past. If there are, I will be delighted to pay them. Also, I have tested this thing so thoroughly that I won't even want the protection of any contract. If I'm not paid immediately I'm just going to give my prophecy to someone else the next time, and that will cost my associate a hell of a lot more than paying me my twenty per cent. Another thing, I don't want to horse around with any small amount of money. I am perfectly capable of doing that myself. I don't want to waste my prophecies on peanuts. I want to be able to clear at least fifty thousand dollars in cash each time I hand down a prophecy. Judging from my record in the ledger, I can't very well do this unless my partner puts in about a quarter of a million dollars."

Mr. Smith looked at his visitor steadily. "It sounds like a great big bunch of crap, but I can't lose too much on that sort of deal, the way you outline it. After all, if worst comes to worst, I've still got a quarter of a million dollars' worth of a stock listed on the Big Board and," he smiled grimly, "none of my money gets out of my hot hands and, without a contract, I guess I can tell you to go to hell any time."

Mr. E.S.P. nodded his head. "You can certainly do that and all you will lose is your profit on the next deal."

Mr. Smith sat thinking. "I don't see how you can make any money if I don't make some for you to get twenty per cent of. Basically, all I'd be doing in each case would be adding a registered stock to my presently rather sizeable portfolio of securities." He looked up at his visitor. "Let's try one out for size and see what happens."

Mr. E.S.P. got to his feet. "The day after tomorrow I'll call you up right after lunch with the name of a stock registered on the Big Board. Immediately, without even waiting five minutes, you must call your broker and tell him to put in an order at the market for a quarter of a million dollars of that company's stock. I can tell you right now that it will close that day at considerably higher than your purchase price. When I call on you to sell, sell immediately, without haggling around too much. The day after you sell, I'll be in for my share. So please have it ready for me in cash."

Mr. Smith was astonished. "In cash?"

"Yes, in cash. I don't want you to be able to trace me by my endorsement on a check. In fact, if everything does not work out perfectly, I will never contact you again. And I can tell you one thing, Mr. Smith, after what happens on this first deal, you'll be tearing down the city to find me and failing. So be sure you do your job exactly the way I have outlined it."

Two days later, shortly after the market opened, Mr. Smith got a telephone call. "Are you still interested in going through with our deal?" asked Mr. E.S.P.

"Yes, I am, what is the stock?"

"Are you going in for the full quarter of a million?"

"Yes, I am."

"Then, the second I hang up the telephone, call your broker and put in an order for a quarter of a million dollars' worth of Seaboard Explosives (name fictitious) and tell him to buy it as fast as the market can absorb it. One thing I want your assurance on. Don't tell anyone about the stock until *after* you have bought yours, or until after noon today—whichever is later. We don't want any freeloaders riding on my prophecy. Anyone you tell after that will, of course, help our stock go up and increase our profits."

Mr. Smith put in the buy order immediately and at 12 o'clock his broker confirmed that he had bought 8,000 shares of Seaboard Explosives at an average price of $28 per share. He was flabbergasted when his broker called up, obviously deeply impressed, to tell him that the stock had closed at $36 and that this gave him a profit of $64,000 on his 8,000 shares in a little over an hour. He immediately got on the phone and tipped off a few of his friends and relatives that Seaboard Explosives common stock looked interesting.

The next day the market in Seaboard Explosives shot upward to $50 and was still going up when Mr. Smith's telephone rang. Mr. E.S.P.'s voice was calm and unexcited. "You've got a profit of one hundred seventy-six thousand dollars," he said quietly. "I want you to call your broker right now, this minute, and tell him to start unloading just fast enough not to rock the market too much. If the market is still over thirty-five after he has unloaded his eight thousand shares tell him to keep right on selling short for you because it is going to continue to drop. Tell him to keep selling until it either gets down to twenty or until he has sold at least eight thousand shares. Then just ride the market down until I call you."

"I'll do it right away."

"One more thing: after you have sold all yours plus the additional eight thousand shares short, then, and not until then, you can tell people what you are doing. You have an obligation to the people you advised to buy the stock and just so they don't move before we do, they might as well make money too. Also, I am coming in at eleven o'clock tomorrow. I want you to have my twenty per cent on the first part of our transaction ready for me in cash. Also, I want the confirmations from your brokers so I can check everything and see what happened."

"I'll have to have a guard from the bank here with that much money."

"That's all right with me."

The next day Mr. Smith was still floored by his good fortune. The sales price on his 8,000 shares of stock averaged out at 49, which gave him a profit of $168,000. A bit more than $33,000 was due his silent partner. He looked at the guard and his leather satchel full of bills. "A man is coming in to pick up this money," he said. "I'll give you five hundred dollars if you can follow him home and find out his name and address."

The guard smiled. "I'd follow old Nick right down through the sewer into the underworld for five hundred dollars," he said.

The guard followed Mr. E.S.P. out of Mr. Smith's office and trailed him down the back street into the subway entrance under the Equitable Building. He tried to make himself inconspicuous. He would play it smart and stay one subway door away from his man so as not to be obvious.

A Grand Central express thundered in and, when the guard saw his man get on, he got on himself. Looking across the tops of the seated people's heads he saw his man standing by the door in the middle of the car. Suddenly, just as the subway doors started to close, the guard saw his man step out onto the station platform. Frantically, the guard put his arm in the way of the door. It obligingly opened again and he stepped out onto the platform himself.

The guard turned around so that he would not be recognized but it was too late. The two of them were standing absolutely alone on the huge platform as the train roared out. Mr. E.S.P. was laughing out loud at him. "You go back and tell your employer, Mr. Smith, that if he ever tries anything like that again it will be the last time he ever sees me."

During the next few days the 8,000 shares Mr. Smith sold short were sold at an average of $45 a share. The stock gradually tumbled to $29 which netted him another $128,000. He gave $25,600 of this to Mr. E.S.P. in cash.

"I've got another prediction for you, Mr. Smith."

"Good, what is it?"

"A representative of the Securities and Exchange Commission is going to come in to see you within the next few days. He will want to know why you bought and sold all those shares of Seaboard Explosives. Just tell him that you have decided to play around in the stock market, that you've got plenty of idle money and that it's going to be one of your professions from now on. If he asks you if anyone gave you any information about the stock just say 'no,' you figured it out yourself."

When the SEC representative came in a few days later it further confirmed Mr. Smith's confidence in the weird, prophetic ability of his new partner.

What Mr. Smith did not know was that he was being run through one of the most complex frauds in the history of fraud. "Mr. E.S.P.," whom we will call Jones, a Ph.D. in mathematics, decided one day that the one science that mathematics had not yet been applied to was fraud. If he could only get one hundred extremely wealthy men to the point where they had complete confidence in him, he would have a vast amount of free capital at his disposal. He tapped his slide rule on the desk. But how could he get the confidence of such men as this?

Suddenly, E.S.P. started scribbling on a piece of paper. What if he picked some future prophecy, any prophecy that was a reasonably even bet, and sent it out to a mailing list of, say, 1600 very wealthy men? He could predict one way with eight hundred letters and the other way with the other eight hundred. No matter which way the prediction went there would be eight hundred men who would think he had prophesied right. He would then do exactly the same thing with another prophecy, splitting the eight hundred down the middle. This prophecy would leave him with four hundred very wealthy men who each thought he had prophesied right *twice*. The third prophecy would leave him with two hundred who would think he had prophesied right three times; the fourth prophecy with one hundred to whom he had prophesied right four times, and so on.

The odds were about even on the Mayor's election, so after the election there were eight hundred wealthy men who thought Jones had prophesied correctly. They did not know, of course, about the eight hundred to whom he had prophesied incorrectly. He then figured another fifty-fifty prophecy; the case of the freight loadings, where the last number had to be either even or odd. He sent out a second letter to the eight hundred who were left, with four hundred prophesying an odd number. This prophecy cut down the list to four hundred and after the next two prophecies he had a list of one hundred very wealthy men to whom he had made five correct prophecies. One of these unfortunates was Mr. Marmaduke Smith.

After contacting them all, Mr. Smith turned out to be one of thirty-one men who were enormously impressed with his five prophecies in a row, with no failures. Each was willing to put at least a quarter million dollars apiece into any stock listed on the Big Board which Mr. E.S.P. chose if there was no contract and if they retained full control of their capital.

This meant, in effect, that E.S.P. had close to eight million dollars which he could toss into any stock he wished on one day's notice. This also meant he had the power to affect radically the price of almost any stock on the Big Board with no commitment or risk on his part. In the case of shares in which there was not a large floating market, he could cause a swing of almost any magnitude he wished in the market price.

By advising his "clients" to buy and sell at different times, Jones could cause some to make money and some to lose money. Under certain circumstances, if they let his advice "leak" to enough outside people, enough new buyers might even get into the picture to assure that all his people would make money at the expense of the general public. Every one of his "clients" who made money had to pay him his 20 per cent share. If they lost a substantial sum, he never called them again and, of course, they did not know who he was or where to reach him.

Another way Mr. E.S.P. made money though was on puts and calls. In this little-known facet of the stock market a mechanism is provided whereby a person can buy an option to buy or sell a certain stock at a price close to its present price, any time in the ensuing six months. In the case of the Seaboard Explosives, which went from $28 to $49, each call Jones purchased would enable him to get 100 shares of this stock at $2800. He could then immediately sell it for $4900 so no capital was required for that part of the transaction and he, in effect, multiplied his investment several hundred per cent.

When Mr. E.S.P. knew the stock had gone up to its highest point (because he had run out of people to advise to buy more of it) he would either sell short and make a profit all the way down as the stock fell or buy a put which, at any time within the next six months, would allow him to force the other party to buy the shares at the inflated market price, even if it had fallen.

While Mr. E.S.P. was juggling his suckers around in Consolidated Electronics he was already working on his next cycle of sixteen hundred new letters for the new crop of suckers. He got a flying start on the next batch of suckers by sending them a prophecy that Consolidated Electronics would go up and then when he pulled out the plug, he sent them another prophecy that it would go down. Of course he was right both times and thus got the first two prophecies of his new series out of the way as a mere adjunct to his last operation. The only limit to Jones's operation was finding the names and addresses of new rich men to send letters to.

FRAUD WITH A TELESCOPE

♠

James Trees sat disconsolately on the overhanging front porch of the Palomar Ski Lodge. It certainly wasn't too damn sensible to spend a vacation at a ski lodge when you couldn't even ski. Trees looked unhappy. That was one of the real troubles of his life, the fact that he had never been athletic. He didn't seem to have either the physical equipment or the coordination to do most of the things everyone else seemed to take for granted. He smiled unhappily. He was one of those people to whom just about everything was a spectator sport. He had to get his fun vicariously by watching other people. He got up and walked to the edge of the balcony. Even that was difficult here because all the skiing and excitement was out on the slopes thousands of feet above him. It was like trying to watch a baseball game from the top of the Empire State Building.

There was a small, stubby-looking telescope perched on a bracket at the edge of the balcony. Trees stared at it. It was one of those things with two eyepieces you saw at so many mountain and seaside resorts. You put in a coin

130

and a clock opened the telescope for a few minutes. It just sat there ticking while you were looking at the scenery and finally, like a parking meter, it shut you off.

Trees fumbled around in his pocket and pulled out a quarter. He pushed the quarter in the slot and put his eye to the eyepiece. He swung the now ticking telescope around to the bottom of the ski lift. It certainly took more guts than he had to get on something like that. What if the damn thing broke when you were hanging up there 100 feet above the ground? It was fun seeing those excited faces. The men and women were really a hell of a lot more interested in each other than in the skiing, no doubt about that. Trees' mouth went down at the corners. His life wasn't too full in that department, either. Women seemed to go for that other type. Something strange about that, because that type didn't necessarily have the most brains.

He swept the telescope up the slope and watched the skiers coming down the regular route. Occasionally the swirling snow blotted out his view, but it was exciting all right. Tremendous speed and all those excited faces. Really a crowd sport with everyone passing everyone else and being sociable and yelling back and forth like a bunch of people at a football game.

Trees swung the telescope over to one of the adjoining slopes. There were a few loners, as there were in every situation, who wanted to get away from the crowd. They were probably lovers or maybe just nonconformists.

The drifting snow, carried by the wind, momentarily blotted out two figures. Trees' eye hardened as he pressed against the eyepiece. There was the son of a bitch all right. He could tell by the red coat, even at that distance. If that is what it took to get everything, he had surely been playing his cards wrong. It was Corbozo and that frightened-looking little wife of his who damned near jumped out of her ski boots every time he looked at her.

Even the management of this place had had a few doubts about letting Corbozo in. After all, a man who had served time for running dope wasn't exactly an asset when you were trying to build a place up socially. He was one of those people who were always on the left side of the law. Always in trouble somehow or other. Always loaded to the eyebrows with money. Wouldn't trust him as far as he could throw an elephant. And yet there was always that fact that he was really loaded. Maybe it was worth it to spend ten years in jail, but it was an awful hard way to earn money.

Trees peered through the telescope. Something seemed to be wrong out there on the slope, although he couldn't see well with all that swirling snow. Corbozo's wife had her hands up over her head protectively as if he was going to strike her. It was a good place to do it all right, where you were hidden from all the rest of the crowd by the ridge in between.

Trees looked sharply into the telescope and then turned abruptly away and went into the restaurant.

It was more than six hours before the news got out, the startling news that Corbozo's wife had been killed out there on the slope. One of those queer accidents that happen to people who don't know very much about skiing.

The highly suspicious police and the top men in the detective bureau rushed out to the scene of the accident. They had finally, and very reluctantly, given up trying to pin anything on Corbozo. His wife had apparently been holding her ski poles wrong, her hands not being through the loops. When she had fallen, one of the poles had twisted around and had got caught under her. It pierced her through the throat.

Although the police were careful to make no accusations, they were very sarcastic in their questioning of Corbozo. The Chief of Police glared at him. "I never heard of such an accident," he said. "Did you actually see it happen?"

"Of course I did," Corbozo said. "I was right next to her."

The Chief looked at him suspiciously. "Why in hell did you have to mess up the snow so much? We can't even figure out what the devil happened from all the tracks back and forth. It looked as if a herd of elephants with skiis on had been trampling up the place."

Corbozo looked at the official coldly. "Exactly what would you do, if the woman you were married to and in love with was bleeding to death right in front of you? I assume you would stay in the same tracks, be very careful not to mess up the snow, and stand there calmly on your skiis without moving."

The coroner reluctantly handed down a verdict of death by accidental causes. The news media made it the big story of the week. A few days later Corbozo, who had moved to a hotel in the town, was given official permission to leave. As he was checking out of the hotel, he felt a tap on his shoulder. Trees was standing behind him. "Mr. Corbozo," the little man said, "I must have a talk with you."

Corbozo waved him aside. "I haven't got anything left to talk to anyone about. Please don't bother me."

Trees' voice was a whisper. "I want to tell you, Mr. Corbozo, what I saw when I was looking at the slope through my telescope the other day."

A few minutes later the two men were talking quietly over a drink at the bar. Corbozo looked at Trees arrogantly. "It would be very little trouble, you know, for me to have you killed. It may be very old and hackneyed, but even in this modern age dead men still tell no tales."

Trees smiled. "From what I knew of your reputation and criminal record, I was absolutely certain you would take that approach." His smile broadened. "So I have prepared for it. I have taken the trouble to write the whole story down in great detail. The day I die or disappear, everyone, including the police, the F.B.I., and the Mayor of East Toledo, Ohio, will hear the whole story. It may not be the best evidence in the world, but, with your past record for selling dope to grammar school kids and murdering people, it will be enough. The courts and the jury will give you pretty short shrift."

Corbozo deflated visibly. "How much do you want?" he demanded. "Not much," said Trees happily. "Not enough to make you want to do very much about it. I want three hundred dollars a month for the rest of my life, payable promptly the first of every month."

Corbozo looked relieved. "But what if you should happen to die—of natural causes, of course. What would happen then to your memorandum about what you saw?"

Trees chuckled. "Copies would go to the police, the F.B.I., the coroner and, in fact, to just about everyone who could do you the most damage. You are just going to have to make it your principal business, Mr. Corbozo, to see that I don't die of natural causes, or any other causes."

♠

Twenty years later Mr. Trees was on his deathbed. The most eminent medical experts had been called from all over the country by Mr. Corbozo to see that he received the best treatment. "How much longer do you give me?" Trees asked them.

"You will be lucky, Mr. Trees, if you last out the day. It may be a matter of hours."

Corbozo was standing by Trees' bed with an anguished look on his face. "I have something very confidential to talk to you about and we have to get these people out of the room."

Trees' voice was very faint. "Has Mr. Corbozo made

arrangements to pay the hospital bill and the services of you gentlemen?" When he had been assured that this had been done, he waved them out of the room.

"Trees," said Corbozo, "I have been giving you three hundred a month for over twenty years. There has never been any trouble about it. It has come in as a nice addition, like cream on the cake. I have also done my damnedest and put out thousands of dollars to keep you alive. You have been a lot happier and a lot more comfortable because of the money I have spent. Also," he pleaded, "you know I have reformed. I have never been in one bit of trouble since that incident on the ski slope. Not even a traffic violation. Why not give me a clean future and get those memorandums out of the safety deposit vaults and destroy them? You've had a nice life because of me. You have also had the pleasure of reforming me and making me a good member of society. Let me plead with you to wipe the slate clean, as your last charitable act."

Trees looked up at Corbozo happily. "There is much in what you say," he admitted. "It has been a happy life and I have even begun to like you, a little bit. I am now wiping the slate clean."

Corbozo looked down at him wide-eyed. "But the memorandums you wrote about what you saw?"

"There are no memorandums. You will remember the telescope was one of those with a clock in it that you put a quarter in. The ticking stopped and it clicked off before I saw anything."

EVERY DOG HAS HIS DAY

♠

Avery Disbro wiped the top of the bar industriously with his cloth. He looked at the result with satisfaction. It shone like a jewel. It was one of the real old-time bars that came down from the pre-prohibition saloon days. A piece of cherry that big nowadays would cost a person a fortune. He looked disconsolately over the empty bar. Business was really lousy. Just one customer sitting down in the corner there drinking beer with his companion. Not much profit margin in that combination, particularly when the companion was a dog that didn't drink anything but water.

Disbro started rearranging the liquor bottles. Maybe he'd better get wise to himself a bit. It was a bad sign when people stopped coming back to your bar. It meant they were not getting something there they thought they were entitled to. He looked at the well-stocked shelves. It certainly wasn't the liquor. Nobody served any better liquor than he and this was one bar that never cut the drinks.

Disbro stopped polishing and looked at his lone customer. He knew what the trouble was all right, and there was no use kidding himself. Even a dumb barkeeper knew the secret of where the profit margin really was. He looked glumly at the reddish-colored dog lying on the floor near his customer. A good percentage of all customers were just paying for the privilege of having someone to yack with, someone who was polite and agreed with them and didn't blow their ass off every time they tried to say something. Disbro's face had an unhappy expression. The bar was the poor man's psychiatrist, no doubt about that, with a long shiny bar and a brass rail instead of a couch and an M.D. with spectacles on his nose. It was just too bad for him he had never liked the conversation part. Maybe he just wasn't the barkeeper type.

Disbro put on an artificially friendly expression. "What kind of a dog is that?" he asked. The customer put down his beer and looked up in surprise. "He is a golden retriever. In fact, one of the best in the United States. He's got a pedigree as long as an elephant's you-know-what."

"You don't say."

The customer looked at him indignantly. "The hell I don't." He started digging into his inside coat pocket and finally got a piece of paper out of his billfold. "Take a look at this," he said, handing it up to the bartender.

Disbro stared at it. It was on the letterhead of the American Kennel Club. It certainly looked very official with all those signatures and seals. It looked exactly like the pedigree of Queen Elizabeth of England, except that every generation had dogs' names. Disbro looked down at the dog. "That must be quite a hunk of dog," he admitted.

"If you don't think so, just turn that piece of paper over and you will see three blue ribbons and a red one pinned to it that he won last week. Farouk, here, is one of the best duck retrievers in the whole country."

Disbro threw his wiping cloth across the bar where it

fell in an untidy wet heap. "Get it, Farouk. Get it," he said. "Bring it back to me."

Farouk looked at the dirty rag with distaste and the customer laughed. "He certainly wouldn't have won those blue ribbons if he could be fooled into thinking a dirty dish rag was a duck," he said. "He knows damned well that if he had gone over and retrieved that dish rag, I would have kicked his ass right into the middle of next week."

Disbro went over and picked up his rag. Nothing was worse than having to drag along a conversation that didn't have anything to it. "I would love to have a dog," he said, "but my wife won't let me." He looked at his customer. That ought to make him feel a little superior, the way the Bartender's Journal was always advising.

To Disbro's surprise, his customer sprang to his feet. "Thank God you said that," he said. "Today is the twelfth of March and it's my wedding anniversary. I damned near forgot it. My wife would really have eaten the fringe off my pants. I'll run over to Michael's and pick up some little present for her." He looked anxiously at the bartender. "Would you mind keeping an eye on Farouk here for a while? I can't take him into the store and if I don't take home something to my wife I am going to really catch it. Farouk is quiet and gentle and he won't cause you any trouble."

Disbro flashed his customer a broad grin. "Feel free. I'll take good care of him. Take as long as you want."

The customer looked apologetic. "Please, I would certainly appreciate it if you don't let him get out of your sight. As you can see, he's an extremely valuable dog and I'd hate like hell to lose him. I'll make it worth your while."

"Don't worry, I'll watch him like he was a bottle of Napoleon Brandy."

The customer went out and Disbro went over and patted the dog. The customer's beer glass was still half full and the dog's pedigree and his ribbons were lying on the table. While Disbro was cleaning up the table another customer came into the bar. He was a tall, distinguished-looking man, impeccably and conservatively dressed. Seating himself on one of the bar stools, he put his foot on the brass rail and opened up a newspaper. He looked at Disbro. "I'll have a double Bushmill's and branch water," he said throwing a twenty-dollar bill on the bar.

Disbro mixed up the drink and set it on the bar. He saw his customer staring at Farouk. He closed up his newspaper. "That is quite a golden retriever you've got there," he said evenly. "I'll bet you really had to pay through the nostrils for that one."

Disbro reached in his pocket. "You sure know your dogs all right. Take a look at this pedigree."

The customer looked at the paper and his eyes widened. "That's quite a dog," he said. "But I knew it the second I saw him. I used to have golden retrievers. One of them was the best hunting dog I ever had. Got killed by an automobile right in front of my house."

"Boy, that's a shame."

A crafty look came into the customer's eye. "I'll tell you what," he said. "You probably don't do much hunting standing here running this bar all day. I'll give you one hundred dollars for this golden retriever."

"He's not mine to sell."

"Then I'll give you two hundred dollars for him and no questions asked."

"If he was mine I would sell him to you quick like a bunny. He was just left here, though, by a guy who went shopping. He'll be back here within the hour."

Disbro felt the other's eyes boring into his.

"I'd certainly like to have that dog." The customer sat thinking. "I'll give you five hundred dollars and no questions asked."

Disbro's voice was beginning to sound desperate.

"But I can't sell you a dog that isn't mine. What would I say to the owner? He would kill me."

The customer leaned over and patted the dog. He carefully examined his teeth and paws. "You couldn't, even for six hundred dollars?" he asked. Suddenly he turned to Disbro. "I'll tell you what I'll do. I'll leave a fifty dollar deposit right here with you in cash. I am over at the Ingram Hotel. If you can get that dog, and I don't give a damn how you get him, bring him over to the hotel and I'll give you the rest of the six hundred dollars. Christ, I've been beating the bushes for a dog like this for two years." The customer laughed wryly. "It doesn't make too much sense being one of the best duck shots in the area if you haven't got an absolutely top-flight dog to find your ducks and bring them back to you. A golden retriever that has won three ribbons and has a pedigree like this one is in the same category as a nymphomaniac whose father owns a liquor store." The customer drained off his double Bushmill's and laid the glass down on the table. "If you can get him for me you will not only get the five hundred and fifty but a little something else for you as well. My name is David Bowen and I am in room four-twenty at the Ingram Hotel."

Disbro looked regretfully at Bowen's retreating figure. That certainly would have been a quick way to pick up six hundred dollars. He shook his head. It would also have been a quick, sure way to get the absolute hell beaten out of himself. And Farouk's master looked like the sort of boy who could do it.

An hour later, Farouk's master came back into the bar with a big package. He shook his head mournfully. "I sure got sold a bill of goods over at the store. A two-hundred dollar dress for my favorite meat-burner. Imagine, two hundred dollars for a dress!" He laughed. "I'll be able to do anything I want after she gets this. The only trouble is I won't have any money to do it with. After I pay for my beer here I am going to have five dollars left to get me through the rest of the week."

Disbro looked at his customer. "Your next drink is on the house," he said, "in celebration of your wedding anniversary. Many happy returns." He drew another schooner of beer. "I certainly have been having a hell of a lot of fun with your dog." A sudden calculating look came into Disbro's eyes. "You wouldn't want to sell him to me for fifty dollars, would you?"

"Fifty dollars?" There was outrage in the man's voice. "My hunting days are over and I certainly need the money more than the dog. You aren't talking about any ordinary dog, though. I wouldn't even sell Farouk's whiskers for fifty dollars."

Disbro laughed. "Well then how about one hundred and fifty? I'm not exactly a rich man, as you can see by my job, and that would use up most of what I've got. I've taken a helluva fancy to Farouk, though."

The customer shook his head. "If you can stretch it to three hundred you've bought yourself a dog. You certainly hit me at the right time. If I wasn't broke three times that much wouldn't touch him."

Disbro took $300 out of his billfold. That was a close one, all right. He just had ten dollars left.

After his customer had departed, Disbro picked up the telephone and called the Ingram Hotel.

"Mr. Bowen will be back in about one hour. If you will leave your name and telephone number, he will call you."

Mr. Bowen never called back and the next time Disbro called, he had checked out of the hotel. The whole scheme turned out to be a complex fraud. It was, in essence, just a complicated way to persuade Disbro to buy a red mongrel dog for $300. Farouk's owner had got him and five other dogs for one dollar apiece from the city dog pound an hour before and had taken Farouk right over to Disbro's bar for the action.

David Bowen was, of course, a confederate, and it was his $50 deposit that clinched everything so that there was no doubt in Disbro's mind concerning his profit in the deal. If the deal hadn't gone through, of course, Bowen would have come back and collected his $50 from Disbro. So it was a "heads I win, tails you lose" proposition.

Bowen and his partner would hit a city at top speed and frequently pull off the dog-selling deal as often as six times in one day. They finally got their procedure geared so beautifully that everything fitted in like a crossword puzzle. They would get the bars all lined up and the one who was going out to buy the present for his wife would go to the next bar in line and offer $600 for the dog he found there. They often cleared $1800 per day on the operation—after taxes.

THE "STOP-LOSS" ORDERS

♠

Mr. Allan Derby, a wealthy businessman from Chicago, went to see his broker two days before he was planning to leave on a European vacation. "I am going to Europe for about three months on a little unwinding vacation with my wife. I don't want to be worried about anything at all while I am gone. As you know, most of my inventory is in blue chips that are going to go fairly well up and down with the market. There is one, though, that certainly isn't in that category and I've got a hell of a big position in it."

The broker nodded gravely. "You are referring, of course, to International Air Craft."

"That's it. It's a good businessman's risk for a person like me, but I don't want to be caught holding the satchel if something goes haywire when I am in Europe. I have fifty thousand shares and, with the present market revolving around forty, that gives me just about a two-million-dollar position in that one stock. It has a hell of a potential and I would hate to unload it, but I just don't want to spend my vacation worrying about it and sleeping with one eye open all the time."

"Why don't you put in a stop-loss order, say at thirty-five? If it hits thirty-five I will automatically start unloading it as fast as I can without cracking the market wide open. There are a hell of a lot of shares outstanding so I ought to be able to dump it pretty swiftly if it falls down to that level."

"That's a good idea. Let's do it that way."

A day or two later, a Mr. Joseph McGittrick was talking to his broker in Denver.

"Bernie," he said, "I am watching so damned many stocks, to say nothing of all the various businesses that I have interests in, that I am either going to have to simplify things a bit, or develop eyes in the back of my head, or blow up and go to the cackle factory."

His broker chuckled. "I have been telling you that for a long time. Why don't you take on fewer deals, but take bigger positions in them? Then you won't always be juggling so much stuff in the air."

"One trouble, Bernie, I've got big profits in most of the things I am in now. On the sound old Rothschild theory, 'Cut short your losses but let your profits run on,' I don't want to get out and take my profits in each case until I have something better to put my money into. Unfortunately, I don't want to be watching the market every single day on each of these securities and having to decide all over again every day what to do about each one."

"Why don't you automate the liquidation side of your problem?"

"What do you mean by that?"

"Just put in a stop-loss order under the market on everything you hold that you don't want to watch all the time. Naturally, with the stock going up and down every day, you don't want to be sold out when the next little wiggle comes along. But you don't want to wake up and find you have taken a big loss, either. Let's take your position in International Air Craft, for example. You are sitting on about twenty thousand shares. The market is around forty, so you have about eight hundred thousand dollars in that stock alone. As I remember, you bought it at fifteen, so you have about a half a million dollar profit you're sitting on. Why don't you just put in a stop-loss order at thirty and forget about it until you need the money for something else?"

McGittrick got up. "I like that. Let's do it. Tomorrow when I come in we can think about the rest of them."

That same day the trust officers of a large Los Angeles bank were discussing a trust indenture. "There is no doubt," the chairman said, "that with all of his toughness in business, the old boy really loved that funny off-beat wife of his."

"It looks like he left her the whole works."

"It looks that way and, as trustees, the only thing unusual about the arrangement as far as we are concerned is that thing about his International Air Craft Corporation stock. Here, let me read it."

In the case of one stock in the portfolio I am leaving to my wife, I wish to limit the unusual freedom which I am giving the trustee in handling the securities in the remainder of the estate. Being intimately connected with the management and policies of International Air Craft, it is my judgment, and I specifically want the trustee to be bound by this judgment, that if the common stock of International Air Craft ever falls as low as 20 on the Exchange, I want the trustee to immediately sell these shares at whatever price can be obtained and reinvest the money in blue chip stocks with growth possibilities. In my judgment if the stock reaches this level something internal will have happened which basically changes the whole potential of this investment. It is my wish that the trustees be bound by this judgment.

"That's a funny one, all right. What is our procedure in a situation like this?"

"Let's just protect ourselves by putting in a stop-loss order for the trust's thirty-five thousand shares of International Air Craft at the old man's stated figure of twenty. That means our broker will have to worry about it for us." The chairman scribbled a note on a piece of paper. "Will you take care of this as soon as our meeting is over?"

"Righto."

A week later a heavy wave of selling hit the shares of the International Air Craft Corporation and the shares rapidly dropped from 40 to 35. Derby's Chicago broker sold his 50,000 shares in accordance with his stop-loss order and the market continued to drop. The decline continued to 30, where McGittrick's Denver broker sold out his 20,000 shares. The market then wavered around 25 for a few days and then dropped almost vertically to 20, at which point the Jacobsen estate in Los Angeles liquidated its 35,000 shares.

The market dropped a few points further to 15 and then the next day the stock opened up twelve points, at 27. In the next few days it climbed all the way back to its original price of 40 and finally stabilized around 45.

There was considerable newspaper publicity concerning the stock's extraordinary gyrations. There was much talk that a "pool" was operating and there was great resentment that an unnamed "they" had "jiggled out" some of the biggest investors in the company.

Allan Derby's Chicago broker was apoplectic. "Allan is going to be as mad as a son of a bitch when he gets back from Europe," he stated flatly. "When he left, the market in International Air Craft was forty. We sold him out under that stop-loss order at thirty-five, so he lost five points there, and the stock is five points above where it was when he left. In other words, he has lost ten points in just a couple of weeks. If he hadn't had that stop-loss order in, Allan would be fifty thousand dollars ahead of where he is now. It's going to be no fun trying to explain the situation to him."

In Denver Joseph McGittrick stormed into his brokerage office. "Great balls of flaming sheet iron!" he shouted. "This is what I get, Bernie, for turning my back on the goddamn stock market for even two weeks on one lousy stock. When I put that stop-loss order in, the stock was 40 and we sold it out at thirty, a loss of ten points. Now it is up to forty-five, so I lost that five points too. I lost fifteen points by just turning my back for two weeks." McGittrick's face flushed a deep red. "That's thirty thousand dollars down the drain with the fish."

In the Los Angeles bank the trust committee had convened in the President's office. The President looked around the table belligerently. "This is the sort of a thing that doesn't do a bank one damned bit of good," he said roughly. "The Jacobsen estate got shaken out of International Air Craft like a bunch of monkeys being shaken out of the tree. It isn't our fault. We certainly can't help it that old Jacobsen had that stop-loss provision in the indenture. But, unfortunately, we are the trustee, and you can't spend all of your time going around explaining stuff like that. It is like the woman who protests too much."

"Mrs. Jacobsen's lawyer has just served notice on us, sir, that she expects the bank to make up the loss which the stock sale has caused the estate. She claims that if we hadn't done anything, just delayed things, it would have saved the estate eight hundred and seventy-five thousand dollars. Instead of losing twenty points they would have gained five on their thirty-five thousand shares."

The bank president snorted. "She hasn't got a leg to stand on. The trustee is only the creature of the trust indenture." He sat thinking. "But a suit like that doesn't do a bank any good. What if the stock had gone all the way down to zero and we hadn't sold it, as ordered in the indenture? We would have been clearly liable for the whole amount."

♠

Three major investors who were, in each case, advised by persons who knew the market intimately, had among them lost $1,655,000 in a period of less than two weeks. Exactly what had happened? Was there a villain? If there was, who was he and how did he do it? How did he make his money?

There was indeed a villain. He was a highly respected member of the New York Stock Exchange. He made an enormous profit on the International Air Craft "jiggle" and his reputation did not suffer one whit as the result of what happened. He was the specialist in International Air Craft stock (all names fictitious).

When the Stock Exchange was started, back in colonial times, its first meeting place was an open space under a buttonwood tree on Wall Street in New York City. The brokers wandered around underneath the tree buying and selling the few securities that were available at that time, securities such as Morris Canal Company stock.

One day one of the brokers fell down and broke his leg. During the six weeks that it was healing up, unable to walk around and bargain with the rest of the stock exchange members, he sat down in a comfortable arm chair and yelled out an announcement, "I can't walk around so I am just going to sit here until my leg heals up. Anyone who wants to buy or sell any shares of Morris Canal stock come over here and I will give them a quote both ways."

To everyone's astonishment, this man, the first Stock Exchange "specialist," made more money in that six weeks

than he had ever made before. He decided to continue being a specialist even after he got well, and it became part of the machinery of the Stock Exchange to have one or more specialists in each stock who handled all the buy and sell orders. He matched them off against each other and took part of the commission which the broker charged his customer. Every specialist had a "book" in which were written all the buy orders, sell orders, stop-loss orders, etc.

Enormous abuses crept into this system and were not eliminated until the founding of the Securities and Exchange Commission in 1934 under a series of statutes which made such abuses illegal and punishable under the federal law.

In the case of the International Air Craft Corporation, the specialist looked at his "book" one day and there he saw Allan Derby's stop-loss order for 50,000 shares at 35 which was 5 points below the market. Joseph McGittrick's stop-loss order for 20,000 shares at 30, and the Los Angeles bank's for 35,000 shares at 20. Instantly he saw that he had a bonanza of the highest order on his hands. He had a row of stop-loss orders on his "book" of a large enough caliber so that each one, as it was "tripped up," would throw a mass of shares on the market which would automatically depress the market to the next stop-loss order, which would, in turn, further depress it to the next one. And so on for as long as they lasted. Only one man on earth knew of this succession of stop-loss orders and that was the specialist. No one else had access to his "book."

The specialist's only problem at this point was to prime the pump. He had to get things started and somehow or other depress the price of International Air Craft from its market of 40 down to 35 where the first stop-loss order, the one put in for Mr. Derby, would be "tripped up."

The specialist immediately sold 10,000 shares at the market. The market fell to 38. He sold another 10,000 shares and it went to 36. It took another 10,000 to push it down to 35, where suddenly Mr. Allan Derby's 50,000 shares were automatically thrown on the market by his stop-loss order. Under this pressure the market immediately started to dive.

Where did the specialist get that 30,000 shares of International Air Craft which he dropped on the market at an average price of $37 a share? He didn't own 30,000 shares, so where did he get the shares necessary to depress the market?

The answer, of course, is that he sold them short. He didn't have any so he borrowed 30,000 shares of International Air Craft and delivered them to the buyers, knowing that he could later buy 30,000 more shares at a cheaper price and return them to the people from whom he had borrowed them. His credit was such that it cost him practically nothing to do this and every point the stock went down profited him $30,000.

When Allan Derby's 50,000 shares hit the market at 35 the price dropped vertically downward to 30, at which point Joseph McGittrick's 20,000 shares were automatically dumped on the market by his stop-loss order.

With the few potential buyers of International Air Craft who were still left in the market wondering what in the name of heaven had happened to the stock and holding back in uncertainty, the stock rapidly dropped from 30 all the way down to 25. It hesitated around 25 and then started to go up as support came in from outside investors who well knew the stock was worth more than 25.

This posed a problem to the specialist, who, of course, wanted the stock to continue to go down still further to the Jacobsen estate's stop-loss order at 20. He was easily equal to this emergency. He already had a profit of 12 points on 30,000 shares, which represented a profit to him of $360,000. He saw no reason to stop there when he had the inside information that there still remained the Jacobsen estate's stop-loss order for 35,000 shares down at 20. With the market wavering at 25 he threw another 30,000 shares on the market in another short sale and the bottom dropped right out of the market.

As the market passed 20, on the way down, the Jacobsen estate's 35,000 shares were automatically dumped on the falling market and added impetus to its fall. It went all the way down to 15 before buyers came into the picture and caused it to start its swift upward climb first to its original price of 40, and then to 45.

It must be pointed out at this juncture that once the decline in International Air Craft stock started, thousands of additional shares were thrown on the market by investors who were frightened or by those who had their shares on margin and did not wish to put up additional collateral. They got "shaken out" by the decline.

The decline was also hastened by a number of false rumors which were leaked out at this critical point to the newspapers. These seriously frightened many investors concerning the future of International Air Craft.

But back to the specialist. Once the Jacobsen estate's 35,000 shares had been dumped on the market, that was the last stop-loss order that could be "tripped up" on his book. The specialist was the only person on earth who knew this extremely valuable fact. He was the only one in the world who knew that as soon as people recovered their sanity and with no more sell orders hanging on the market, there was just one way the stock could go and that was straight up. He was, of course, short 60,000 shares which he had borrowed in order to make his short sales. He would eventually, of course, have to give equivalent shares back to the owners from whom he had borrowed them originally at 37 and 25. With the market at

15 the specialist already had a paper profit of $960,000 on his "investment."

As soon as the 35,000 Jacobsen shares hit the market, the specialist started buying for his own account. Every share offered on the market was bought by him personally until he had the 60,000 shares which he eventually had to give back. He was not only able to buy back the whole 60,000 shares he was short, at an average price of 18, but he also accumulated 60,000 more shares "long" for the rise that only he knew had to come. He then sat back in his chair and watched the market shoot back up past its original price of 40 to 45. Being the only man on earth who knew positively that it had to go up, he kept buying shares on margin which, as they went up, added to his already enormous profit.

The specialist's total profit on this complex and extraordinary operation amounted to a little over $3,000,-000. It was made in a period of a few days with no capital risk whatsoever and required practically no work on his part. The ordinary run-of-the-mine confidence man pales into insignificance compared to the old-time market rigger in the days before the Securities and Exchange Commission.

It is well to point out here that such a fraud is no longer possible. If a stock moves in an erratic, preposterous manner, the Securities and Exchange Commission now steps in, scrutinizes all the purchase and sell orders and swiftly finds out who is responsible. Anyone who "tripped up the stop-loss orders" now would almost certainly find himself tripped up and facing a long stretch in the federal penitentiary. On top of that he would be subject to damage suits for recovery from his victims.

WHEN THE CHAUTAUQUAS FOLDED

The following story was a favorite of Elliot Ness, the Cleveland, Ohio, Safety Director, the hero of *The Untouchables*, the man who caught Al Capone and who was one of our nation's greatest experts on fraud.

♠

In the 1920's the old Chautauqua circuits finally folded because of radio and the movies. Hundreds of talented performers of the platform and stage suddenly found themselves jobless. One desperate actor whom we will call Hamletoff actually played the part of a live gorilla in the zoo of the large Middle Western city of Megopolis.

When Mainwaring, his agent, first offered him the job he was absolutely outraged. "Me!" he shouted, his face red with fury. "I, who have played Hamlet all over the world with top billing, get into a smelly old gorilla skin and actually pretend I am a live gorilla? Absolutely not." He started to stalk out of the room like Banquo's ghost.

155

Mainwaring shook his head sadly. "When your whole industry gets snatched out from under you like a rug," he said, "you've just got to adapt or perish. It's the only booking we have in our whole shop. Frankenstein, the famous gorilla who was loved by thousands of children in Megopolis, got the green-apple quickstep last night and dropped dead. There's going to be a fearful scandal when the kids find out, and the zoo director tells us he's almost sure to be fired. He sent us the gorilla's skin all cured and fitted with zippers and I've got to fill it up with a real live body right away. One of our temperance lecturers, who has never played the part of a gorilla, is begging for the chance, so take it or leave it."

Mainwaring paused. "Why in God's name be so all-fired high-toned? Nobody will know it's you and your famous profile all wrapped up in the gorilla skin. You can loaf all day, do a few tricks, and eat your breakfast cereal for the kids. And the pay's not bad at all."

The next morning the actor was in the gorilla's cage when the children arrived. Hundreds of them were massed around the cage. The hairy skin felt hot and scratchy and hung loosely all over him but it was a lot better than starving. Hamletoff waved at the kids with a loose, baggy motion. It wasn't like Shakespeare, but the applause was terrific. That was what steadied him. It was a helluva lot like the old Chautauquas. By God, he would give the enthusiastic little bastards their money's worth.

Hamletoff tied his napkin around his neck with a hairy flourish and ate his breakfast cereal to a rising crescendo of enthusiastic shouts. The job wasn't too bad after all, he admitted to himself. If it wasn't for the fierce-looking lion in the next cage, it might turn out to be a good rest. One slap through the bars from that baby, though, and it would be lights-out forever. The lion's teeth looked like huge white jackknives.

The actor beamed at the cheering children. They

were sort of cute, at that, yelling and screaming that way. By God, he would lay them right out in the aisles. He jumped up and grabbed the horizontal bar that stretched across his cage. Slowly he started swinging back and forth. He chinned himself three time and increased his swing. The kids went absolutely wild. Frankenstein had never done anything like that before.

Hamletoff swung higher and higher. It reminded him of those glorious days when he was captain of his college gymnastic team. What in hell did a gorilla do for an encore? Intoxicated by the hysterical applause, he swung even higher. Finally, harking back to his youth, he started circling the bar vertically in a giant swing.

Suddenly there was a sickening snap and the bar broke, right in the middle. The actor flew through the air and landed with a thunderous crash. He lay there stunned for a moment and then he slowly opened his eyes. He closed them spasmodically and then opened them again. He had fallen into the lion's cage. The lion was standing over him with one huge paw planted in the middle of his chest. The actor frantically twisted away. "Help! Help! Help!" he shouted.

The lion jumped on top of him and jammed his paw over Hamletoff's mouth. "Shut up! You crazy bastard," he whispered furiously. "Do you want us both to lose our jobs?" It was the voice of Mainwaring, his agent.

DANIEL DREW
He Cheated the Mighty

♠

It was shortly after the War of 1812. A herd of over 1,000 head of cattle was moving slowly over the road from Ohio into New York State. It was a nondescript herd but its owner, Daniel Drew, was more so: A nondescript man on a nondescript horse wearing nondescript homespun clothes, a battered felt hat and, incongruously enough, urging his nag on with a green umbrella, which he clutched in his right hand.

A few days later Daniel Drew and his herd arrived at the New York buying station of Henry Astor, the brother of John Jacob Astor. Astor looked over the lowing herd. "That's a fine herd of cattle," he admitted grudgingly. He quoted Drew a premium price per pound which was quickly converted into cash for Daniel Drew as the cattle were weighed and put into the stockade.

The next morning Astor looked aghast at what he had bought. As thin a beaten-up, scrawny-looking herd of cattle as had ever been seen in his stockyard.

A swift investigation on Astor's part disclosed that

158

for three days, as the herd was being driven down the dusty New York road, Daniel Drew had ordered his drovers, under no conditions, to let the cattle drink any water.

The last two days of the drive had turned into a desperate battle between the cattle and the drovers, which reached a crescendo whenever they passed a stream or creek. To make matters worse, Drew had the drovers mix salt with their feed. The cattle finally became so maddened for water that they were almost impossible to handle.

Just before they came to Astor's weighing station, Drew spied a shallow creek. He signalled to his drovers. "Let them drink all they want," he cried.

The cattle plunged into the creek and drank and drank and drank and drank until they almost burst. Drew, who had never learned to write, figured rapidly in his head. If each animal drank a cubic foot of water it would add over 30 tons to the weight of his herd. Tons which, after the sale to Astor, would quickly vanish. A nice profit, indeed.

Astor, outraged when he saw the herd the next day, was said to have roared like a bull. "I have been sold watered stock," he shouted to all who would listen, and the term has become part of the vernacular of Wall Street.

As for Daniel Drew, his profit on the transaction was enormous, made still more so by the fact that he never bothered to pay the farmers back in Ohio for their cattle.

Drew prospered in the cattle business, opened up a drovers' tavern, and started a wholesale meat market of his own. He soon advanced to more challenging fields.

Robert Fulton's steamboat had established itself as a success and the State of New York had given the Fulton syndicate a monopoly on all steamboat operations in New York waters. "Commodore" Vanderbilt, operating a boat called the *Bellona,* which was based in Jersey City, ran his boat brazenly into the New York waters covered by the Robert Fulton monopoly. A master publicist before public relation firms had even been thought of, he flew a big flag from the smokestack of the *Bellona* with the legend, *"New Jersey Must Be Free."* He then complained through the newspapers that the public was being squeezed by the Fulton syndicate and that the New York monopoly should be abolished.

The public pressure on the Fulton syndicate finally became so great that it eventually, with great reluctance, for they knew he was a battler, haled Vanderbilt into court charging violation of their monopoly. Vanderbilt retained the golden-tongued Daniel Webster to carry his case to the United States Supreme Court and finally won on the grounds that the Fulton monopoly was unconstitutional. This decision opened up the waterways of the fledgling country. Vanderbilt was widely hailed as the savior of the public.

Taking immediate advantage of his victory, Vanderbilt decided to enlarge his operations. He swiftly drove his competitors to the wall by successive rate slashes and finally forced them to buy him off.

Daniel Drew decided he had to share in Vanderbilt's good fortune, somehow. He purchased an old, inefficient, and very dilapidated steam boat known as the *Water Witch*. He painted her up and started taking passengers and freight at rates much lower than Vanderbilt's. The first year he lost over $10,000 and Vanderbilt was said to have given him quite a ribbing about it.

To Vanderbilt's astonishment, Drew completely ignored his losses and lowered his rates still further. He got out ads to the effect that the *Water Witch* would take passengers all the way from New York City to Albany for only twenty-five cents. He then started getting out releases, fliers, and placards which attacked Vanderbilt for his unfair high rates and compared him to a bloodsucker feeding on the public.

Vanderbilt, badly damaged, was only too glad to pay Drew an exorbitant price for the *Water Witch*, a price which not only paid for all of Drew's losses but gave him a substantial profit.

Many years later, when both men were extremely wealthy, Vanderbilt realized one day that he, at long last, had Daniel Drew in his power. He would get his revenge for the *Water Witch* fraud Drew had pulled on him years before.

The two men were battling for control of the Erie Railroad. The competition between the two giants had boomed the railroad's common stock up to such a height that Drew suddenly decided he could make more money by selling his stock than by fighting for control of the railroad. He sold not only all the shares he owned but, knowing that the bottom would drop out of the stock when the battle for control was over, he started selling thousands of shares of the company's stock short. In order to do this, he had to borrow stock to deliver on his sales with the understanding that he would return the stock to the lenders later. He was sure he could buy the shares cheaper later and make money on the borrowing operation.

Commodore Vanderbilt, his eye focussed only on getting control of the Erie Railroad, kept buying stock and Daniel Drew, knowing it would fall, kept selling it short in a situation which obviously could not go on forever. One day the Commodore found to his astonishment and delight that he actually owned more shares than had ever been issued by the railroad. In other words, he had cornered the market in Erie Railroad common stock. Vanderbilt knew, of course, that this put Drew in a frightful position. He had sold more shares than there were in existence. When he tried to buy shares to give back to those from whom he had borrowed, the only seller would be Commodore Vanderbilt himself. He could, if he wished, demand one million dollars a share. The Commodore swiftly applied the screws.

An indescribable confusion engulfed the Stock Exchange as the news of the corner got out. As the price of Erie stock shot up through the roof, there was absolute bedlam, a scene more reminiscent of a circus than of a stock exchange.

Mysteriously, more and more Erie Railroad shares appeared to be coming on the market from somewhere. Obviously the source was not Vanderbilt, who would naturally not act to break his own corner. In fact, he was still buying all the shares that were offered as fast as they came onto the floor.

Finally, when one broker grabbed a share of Erie Railroad common stock from another, he noticed with astonishment that the ink on the certificate actually smeared under his fingers! He let out a wild yell. Someone was apparently printing the shares and unloading them on the floor of the exchange before the ink even had time to dry.

The news spread like an explosion and the bedlam that engulfed the exchange was like nothing that had ever been seen before in its history. Men were running hatless and coatless in all directions screaming and yelling as the whole stock market, not only Erie Railroad common, but all other stocks as well, fell vertically downward. As one historian put it, "high above the bedlam sounded the mad roars of Commodore Vanderbilt, who was said to have lost $7,000,000 in fifteen minutes."

When the story came out, and probably the facts are not all in yet, it was again Daniel Drew who was the villain. An imaginative innovator in the field of finance, he had invented a new financial mechanism, the convertible bond. Under the indenture of this bond the holder

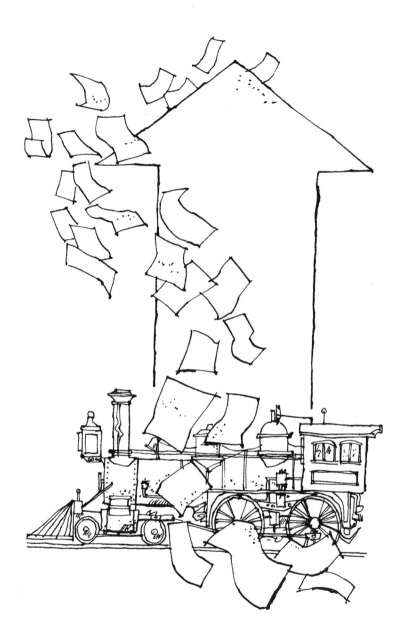

could, whenever he desired, ask that his bond be converted into common stock. This increased the value of the bonds because it combined the security and prior position of conventional bonds with the speculative possibilities of the common stock into which they could be converted.

Although historians are not quite in agreement as to the facts, Daniel Drew had evidently figured out the whole thing in advance. When his battle for control of the Erie with Vanderbilt started, he figured that Vanderbilt would first keep on buying the stock because he wanted control. Then when he saw that he could ruin his old enemy, Daniel Drew, by cornering the stock (and making him pay any amount he wished to cover) Drew figured that Vanderbilt would buy and keep buying even after he had control, to firmly establish his corner.

Drew, firm in the knowledge that he could always convert his Erie Railroad bonds into common stock and break the corner, kept selling short and shovelling shares down Commodore Vanderbilt's throat, knowing full well that the bottom would fall out of the market when the corner didn't develop. What it all boiled down to was that there were some 100,000 shares of Erie common stock shares that could be created by the conversion of the convertible bonds hanging over the market. Vanderbilt did not know these were being converted. It was these shares suddenly pouring onto the market which smashed Vanderbilt's corner.

The "Erie Panic," as it was called, caused widespread bankruptcy and unhappiness throughout the country. One of its outcomes was the sad fact that 60 years later the Erie Railroad had not paid a single dividend on its common stock.

Years later, General Daniel Sickles, the hero who lost his leg commanding the federal artillery at the Battle of Gettysburg, decided to get Daniel Drew off the Erie Board of Directors somehow. Sickles was a rough fighter and he had plenty of financial support. The battle was an epochal one. Nothing seemed to work though until one day Sickles had an idea. He arranged a meeting with Drew. "Mr. Drew," he said, "we are all substantial holders of Erie Railroad common stock. You are probably the biggest holder of all. Most of the stockholders think you are a crook, so there is nothing that would make the stock go up faster in price than the announcement of your resignation from the Board.

"I'll bet it would make the price of Erie common go up ten or fifteen points. You could make a million dollars overnight by just resigning."

That was the sort of talk that Daniel Drew had a keen ear for. He told Sickles he would think about it. Then, with a view to selling out at a profit after the news of his resignation was issued, he secretly bought thousands of shares of Erie Railroad stock through intermediaries.

Later, Drew was at a meeting at which many of the richest men of the city were present. As was his custom, he took off his red cotton bandanna and wiped his brow with it. A crumpled piece of paper fell out onto the floor. One of the tycoons present put his foot on the paper and stood there until Drew had left the room. Many people had seen him do this, so when Drew finally left they crowded around to see what was on the paper. It said, "Buy all of the Erie Railroad common stock you can get your hands on."

In a twinkling, the room was empty and the rush of buy orders coincided with the announcement of Daniel Drew's resignation from the Board of Directors. The market went up out of sight and Daniel Drew unloaded at the very top. He was said to have made over five million dollars out of his resignation from the Erie Railroad Board of Directors.

Despite his cleverness, Drew was caught, as were

many of the wealthiest men of that time, in the panic of 1873, and finally got his comeuppance.

After the panic, his assets were listed as follows:

Watch and chain	$150
Sealskin coat	$150
Other wearing apparel	$100
Bibles and Hymn books	$130

To make matters worse, the people whom he had failed to pay for their cattle more than sixty years before came trooping into New York City from Ohio to collect their ancient debts.

THE CASE OF THE LIQUID ASSETS

♠

A hard-sell, high-pressure salesman named Smith was once approached by a very studious college friend who was a Ph.D. in chemistry. "I've just invented a remarkable solvent," the friend said. "It is perfect for cleaning expensive and delicate furs. One has only to immerse the fur in a tank of this liquid. The next morning the fur will be completely clean. No rubbing or special treatment is necessary to take off spots. Even the most expensive and delicate fur of all, chinchilla, is not hurt one bit by my solvent. In fact, it actually improves the appearance of the fur."

Smith looked skeptical. "What's in the liquid?" he asked.

"It's a secret formula, one of those complex organic things that even the quantitative and qualitative chemists couldn't possibly figure out. Any cleaner who had my secret fluid would have no trouble cornering the fur-cleaning market. It's worth millions of dollars a year."

Smith's head jerked up. He looked at Jones with incredulity. "Millions of dollars a year? How do you know your cleaner is as good as that?"

Jones beamed. "I knew you'd ask that." He held up a single silver fox pelt. "This is the most expensive fur I can afford as a demonstrator," he said regretfully. He poured a bottle of milk into a bowl and thrust the fur under the surface of the milk. He then cracked two eggs into the bowl and, using the fur as a stirrer, he mixed the solution into a messy yellow froth. Then, while Smith watched in fascinated silence, he poured half a bottle of red wine and a cup of oil from the crankcase of his car into the bowl. He sloshed the fur vigorously around in the sticky, black and red goo.

Jones held up the fur. "Looks exactly like a sewer rat that has been run over by a steam roller. How would you like the job of cleaning that?"

Smith looked at the matted, hairy mass with horror. "I wouldn't even know where to start."

Jones poured some clear liquid from a bottle into a clean bowl and put the fur into the liquid. He sloshed it gently back and forth. "My solution is not only unin-flammable," he said, "but it doesn't even harm your hands. It is just as good for them as it is for the fur."

After the fur had dried it looked even better than it had in the beginning.

Smith was deeply impressed. Not a trace of the awful mess remained. The delicate fur was completely restored. "How much does the liquid cost?" he demanded.

"The dirt is now all in solution in the liquid," the chemist smiled triumphantly. "That's the best part of the whole thing. It just doesn't make any difference how expensive the liquid is because you can reuse it any number of times. When it gets dirty, you just boil it through a regular commercial still and it is just as good as new. All the dirt remains behind in the still."

Smith was fascinated. "Exactly what's in the liquid?" he demanded.

Jones shook his head regretfully. "That is always

going to be my secret," he said. "We can form a partnership if you want, with you doing the selling and operating the company and I providing the liquid. We will split everything fifty–fifty."

Smith was outraged. "But I'll be working a full day every day and you'll just be sitting on your bucket collecting half the profits."

Jones looked back at him steadily. "I've already done my work," he said. "Inventing the liquid. Enough for a whole lifetime. If you want to be my partner, you've got to do all the work from now on."

Their company was an instant success. Their liquid did a perfect job every time and Smith was a demon salesman. They eventually captured most of the fur-cleaning market in the city.

From the first Smith had decided to cheat his partner out of his share of the profits some way, if only he could get the formula for the magic liquid. He took a vial of it over to a local chemist for analysis. After a few days the chemist threw up his hands. "There are some things that just defy analysis," he said, "and this is one of them. It is like Angostura Bitters or this chili sauce that comes from New Iberia, Louisiana. If I could analyze either of those I could make myself a millionaire. Everyone has tried and failed." He shook his head. "About all I can tell you is that it is a complex mixture of hydrocarbons, probably scores of them."

Discouraged, Smith started stealing drums of the secret solvent from their reserve warehouse. The liquid could be used forever; all you had to do was redistill it when it got dirty. If he could steal enough liquid to run several plants, he could start a competing company and run off with all their profits. After all, it was *he* who did all the selling and *he* who ran the company. He could put himself on easy street for the rest of his life if only he could steal enough of the liquid.

Smith laid his plans very carefully. After he had stolen enough drums of the solvent for his proposed operation, he purchased a commercial still that would keep the liquid fresh forever. He rented a factory and some office space and poured the precious liquid he had stolen into the huge factory vat. He then decided that all he needed for a dramatic start was a good publicity story in the newspapers.

Smith went to their best customer, a local department store, and said he was terminating their partnership and opening a competing operation where the customers' furs would be cleaned at a lower cost. He offered to clean the most valuable fur coat in the customer's store, a chinchilla worth over $70,000 absolutely free of charge, with a newspaper man photographing and reporting on the whole operation.

The store owner, delighted with the publicity possibilities, sent the precious fur coat over to the new cleaning factory in a special Brink's truck. With flashbulbs popping and a sizable crowd assembled, the newspapermen watched their biggest advertiser ceremoniously deliver the precious coat. They stood there fascinated while the beautiful fur was lowered carefully into the secret liquid.

The news story turned out to be much bigger than anticipated . . . because when the chinchilla coat was lowered into the liquid there was a moment of inaction. Then suddenly, to everyone's astonishment, there was a violent bubbling and hissing. The secret liquid boiled up tumultuously as if it were boiling hot. To everyone's horror the fine, silky hairs of the precious coat dissolved completely and fell to the bottom of the tank as a dirty brown sludge. All that was left of the coat were scores of pieces of bare leather sewn together with thousands of tiny stitches.

Smith's new business was completely ruined on the day it started, not only by the newspapers' hilarious publicity but by the fact that he was financially ruined by the $70,000 lawsuit filed against him the next day for the ruined chinchilla coat. The day after that the police picked him up on a grand larceny charge for stealing the drums.

It developed that his partner, the chemist, finding that the drums of his precious liquid were disappearing, hired an industrial counter-intelligence agent to find out exactly what was going on. When the agent discovered that it was the partner who was stealing the drums, he suggested that he have him arrested on a grand larceny charge and terminate their partnership. The chemist, outraged, shook his head. "We can do that later. Let's have some fun with him first."

He concocted a special fur-destroying liquid and added it to all of the drums that his partner was stealing.

WALLS OF REAL GOLD

A rich San Francisco businessman was approached by an almost hysterically excited prospector who had come rushing into town with a claim to "one of the richest gold mines ever found in this area." "I don't even begin to have the money to mine it," he admitted. "And even if I did, I don't know a goddamned thing about mining. I don't want to take any chance of getting cheated out of my claim, but I do need help and I need it bad."

The businessman was understandably suspicious. "So you'd like to sell me some gold mine stock, eh what?" His voice was heavy with sarcasm.

The old prospector's heavily lined face bristled with indignation. "I certainly do not," he shouted. "And you can go straight to hell. I'm an old-time rotgut prospector, not a promoter, and what's more, I'm one of those rare animals, a *successful* prospector." He glowered at the businessman. "This is an absolutely proven, blocked-out mine with a legally recorded title that is going to make me and anyone who helps me exploit it a hell of a lot of money. There is no secret about this mine at all and nothing funny or offbeat about it. I'll show it to everyone and let them see for themselves." The prospector got up to leave. "I approached you only because you have the reputation of being a smart, honest man who has money available for businesses where you can supply the capital and the management. If you turn me down, I'm just going to put an advertisement in the *San Francisco Chronicle* telling my whole story and asking for help." The prospector held up a piece of paper. "In fact, I've already written it. You'll see what you missed when you see what happens."

The businessman looked at the crudely worded ad. It certainly wasn't good grammar but it would get results, all right. If the old rascal really had a mine. "I'll take a look at your mine," he said grudgingly. "If I like it, though, exactly what do I get for my money?"

"You get full title to the mine and we'll record your title in your name right at the County Recorder's office. I won't sell you the property, though, until you sign the contract agreeing to develop the mine, provided I am right that there is gold there in workable quantity and agreeing that I will get half of the profits after reasonable expenses."

"So I get full title to your claim, eh what? How much do I have to pay for the property?"

"One hundred thousand dollars and your signature on this contract agreeing to work the mine and divide equally with me."

They drove out to the mine and the businessman was surprised to see a locked iron door at the entrance to the tunnel. The prospector was grim-faced. "I found some of the local red necks sneaking out here at night with pickaxes stealing my ore. It's a hell of a note to work hard all your life to finally strike it rich once and then have a bunch of cheap chiselers try to screw you out of it."

The two men walked a quarter of a mile down into the old shaft until they finally came to what was obviously a recent digging. The light from their lamps was reflected in hundreds of tiny little facets from the surface of the rocks.

"Those bright specks, believe it or not, are pure gold," the prospector said. "If the original owner had only had the guts and luck to dig ten more feet, *he* would have found it instead of me. We've just barely cut into the edge of the lode." He pointed to a clean-cut round hole about an inch in diameter. "We know the ore goes back over a hundred feet because we've core drilled it back that far." The old prospector smiled happily. "There's enough gold from here up to the end of that boring to give me all the money I'll be able to spend the rest of my life." He flashed a toothless, happy grin. "And when I get into town I'm a pistol. I can really spend the money." His grin broadened. "And for all we know, the lode might go on for hundreds of feet farther."

The businessman tried not to show his astonishment. He stood, thinking. With the gold right in the solid rock that way it obviously couldn't be a "salted" mine. He flashed his light around. Maybe the shining flecks were not gold, though. "How do I know this showing is not fool's gold?" he demanded. "Iron pyrites?"

The old man laughed. "The same way I know, by getting it tested. I haven't been an old-time prospector this long to get sucked in by that obvious sort of crap." He opened up his pen knife and handed it to the business- man. "Be my guest and flake off as many of the specks as you want and have them tested yourself by your own chemist. If they are not gold, I guarantee to eat them right at noon on the public square."

With considerable difficulty the businessman gouged fifteen or twenty random pieces out of the hard flint-like matrix and wrapped them up in his handkerchief. He looked around him. There were literally thousands of them. Must be one hell of a concentration of something all right. If it turned out to be gold—holy Jesus.

The next day his chemist told the businessman that

the specks were pure gold. That afternoon he paid the old prospector one hundred thousand dollars and had the property legally transferred to himself at the County Recorder's office. He signed the contract agreeing to work the mine and split the profits with the prospector. The businessman was delighted with what he now realized was going to be the most profitable deal of his life.

Several weeks later tests showed that the gold in the walls, genuine as it was, was only skin deep. It was scattered at random on the surface. It later developed that the "prospector" had fired gold dust and gold granules out of his twelve-gauge shotgun against the hard stone face. At just the right distance with just the right load of powder and a wide-open choke, the gold specks were tightly sintered into the wall in a startlingly realistic manner.

THE GOERING PASS BOOK FRAUD

♠

Starke Jones reached over and pressed the secret button under his desk. There was a faint smile on his lips. Even when you were grown-up, intelligence work was fun. And these little boy scout things were all part and parcel of it. In what other profession, by God, did you have a button hidden under your desk just for summoning your bodyguard?

The door flew open and was completely filled by the huge figure of a man who weighed well over two hundred and fifty pounds. The monster's right hand was in his coat pocket in a position that looked so studiedly natural it was patently phony. After a lightning glance around the room a look of disappointment passed over the heavy face.

Jones laughed. "No German spies to shoot the buckets off of this morning," he said.

The serious look on John Black's face vanished. His voice was deep and melodious. "Maybe some time," he said hopefully.

"You said yesterday you had something important to talk to me about."

"Oh that." Black sat down in the chair in front of Jones' desk. It creaked ominously. "I've just been turning some things over in my mind. Things I thought might interest you."

Jones leaned back in his chair. Black was the damnedest combination, really, that they had anywhere in the organization. Two hundred and fifty pounds and an absolutely dead shot. So swift on the draw he could actually beat the electronic shooting machine out at Area G. Built like a Sherman tank to smash great big things up into little messy pieces.

Jones put his feet up on his desk. But that wasn't the really funny part. In many ways Black had the most subtle mind in the whole shop. A Sherman Tank with a genius I.Q. A criminal waste, really, using a mind like that as a bodyguard. A painfully typical example of using a man's most obvious characteristic. Jones looked at Black critically. He would have to try him out on something cerebral and see what flew out of the machinery.

The heavy man had an amused look on his face. "It all boils down to one thing, Starke," he said. "The United States is a completely new bunny in the spy war. We are all a bunch of talented amateurs, really, without too much practical experience. You are always yelling and screaming, Starke, about the spy war being the 'unorthodox war.' That's just a big bunch of fancy verbiage. All we have done is to sit down with a new set of rules that are a bit more liberal than the rules of the Hague Convention. They are almost as definite, though. It is sort of like the situation with wrestling. If two men fight without any rules, someone immediately loses an ear or an eye or gets a broken neck. In order to turn it into a sport you have got to have rules that keep people from getting hurt beyond a certain point."

Black paused. "So you have the college wrestling rules. They are the Hague Convention rules of that particular sport. Then you get busy and learn a bunch of wrestling tricks that comply with the rules. Unconsciously you build up a feeling in your mind that that's fighting. It takes more than a little imagination to see that it isn't really fighting at all. It's more like playing checkers."

Black laughed his deep, booming laugh. "It is just as if the world's heavyweight wrestling champion would make the perfectly natural mistake of tackling one of our Area G graduates on the basis that he was a set-up. When he got out of the hospital six months later he would at least know one thing. He would know that wrestling wasn't fighting."

Jones looked at Black impatiently. "You are sitting there building a slow fire under me as if I were an old Civil War steam locomotive. You want to suggest something unorthodox. How about being really unorthodox and suggesting it right away without any more orthodox build-up?"

Black chuckled. "All right, I will start by being modest. I have dreamed up a scheme that would save Uncle Sam a billion bucks and a lot of lives in its war with Hitler."

"A billion bucks?"

"Yes. A billion bucks. We are so busy putting people under cover, teaching them how to blow each other's buckets off, tearing up the material in their waste paper baskets, warning them not to meet tardy contacts, setting up cut-outs and camouflages to operate through, and charging around like a bunch of hungry ferrets, that we are not thinking about some of the obvious things. Things that don't need that sort of crap."

"Such as what?"

"How about taking an entirely different approach in a new dimension? We know that anything we could do to cause conflict in Germany's top echelon would slow up their war effort and help ours. We also know that there is a whale of a lot of tension in their top echelon already. Like most dictators, Hitler has a group of courtiers right under him who are vying for his favor. First of all, there is Hermann Goering, the head of the German Air Force. Then there is Heinrich Himmler, who is the head of their Internal Security. Then there is Goebbels, the Propaganda Minister, and General Nicolai, their Coordinator of Intelligence. Most of these characters cordially hate each other and would jump at any chance to rev up the old donkey engine and pull the rug out from under one of their rivals. If we know this, and we do, why don't we manufacture some ammunition for them to use against each other. If we could get them climbing all over each other at top echelon, it might ease things up a bit for us."

"I'll buy that, but how do we do it?"

"How about taking a hundred thousand dollars of our unvouchered funds and sticking them in a bank in some neutral country, let's say Argentina. We would deposit the money to the account of Field Marshal Hermann Goering and then tip off his arch enemy, Heinrich Himmler, through conventional spy channels. We could plant the story that Goering felt the war was lost and was already beginning to sneak his money out of the country. We could see that Himmler got evidence in the form of deposit slips, a bank pass book, etc."

Jones' voice was sarcastic. "How do you propose to get Marshal Goering to sign his deposit slip?"

"That's what we have all these forgers for who are cooling their heels down in the Atlanta Penitentiary. We'll just get one of the best of them to copy Fatso's signature out for us."

"Where are you going to get an original signature of Goering's for our forger to copy?"

"From the State Department. They have his signature on all sorts of papers involving treaties about aircraft and stuff like that."

"How would you make the deposit? It isn't every day that a bank in Argentina gets a deposit from a German Field Marshal. The first thing they would do when they got the deposit would be to write the old boy a letter of acknowledgement and thanks and that would blow the whole show sky high."

"We could do it exactly the way you would if you wanted to open a secret account in Argentina. We would send a representative down there with full authority to talk and act. He would emphasize the enormous importance of secrecy, imply that this was just the first little trickle of the vast sums that would soon come pouring into the bank if everyone showed they could be discreet enough. The representative would emphasize the fact that under no circumstances was anyone ever to communicate directly with the Field Marshal."

"Who would make all these arrangements and who would go down to Argentina with the money?"

"I would."

"You?"

"Why not? I speak and write German better than Goering. And besides, what good am I around here being the bodyguard of a boss who never gets shot at? I think you should either manage to get yourself shot at once in a while or assign me to a more challenging job. You are so damn gung ho about your cover no one even knows who the hell you are. Here I am, two hundred and fifty pounds on the hoof, in one of the most interesting wars in all history, sitting on my ass with my hand on a gun which never goes off."

Jones laughed and took his feet down from the desk. "John, you've bought yourself a job. You talk about our unvouchered funds, though, as if they grew on bushes. A hundred thousand dollars is too much to blow on one operation. Even one like this. I am going to start you off with thirty thousand dollars for the Goering deposit. You work out the details. For security reasons we'll give it the five-letter code group 'OPERATION FATSO.' "

Six weeks later, they were sitting in the same room. Jones had a deep feeling of accomplishment. They had certainly found themselves a real brain in the spy business, no doubt about that. He looked approvingly at Black. "You seem to have pulled off quite a coup."

Black shook his head. "It was touch and go several times. Trying to get the Goering signature from the State Department without any security leaks was like trying to goose a ghost. Once I got that, though, it was no trouble getting the deposit slip made out down at the Atlanta Penitentiary. That place is just loaded with talent. Going down to Argentina to make the deposit was just a nice vacation. Gave me a chance to add a few Argentine girls to my collection."

"How about getting the pass book into Himmler's hands?"

"No sweat at all. I used Schwartz, the double we've been paying in our labor espionage set-up. We've sent enough really important information back to the Germans through him that they're fully convinced he's on their side. He said Himmler's representatives really drooled when they saw the photostat of our bank pass book with the Field Marshal's signature on it."

"Why has everything taken so long?"

"Because Himmler wasn't born yesterday. He trusts Schwartz, but he didn't want to get caught out in left field by a phony plant. He is the sort of fellow though who doesn't sit on his hands when he gets something hot like this. He immediately sent an agent to Argentina by submarine to check it all out. He made sure Goering really did have an account at the bank. When Himmler got his cable saying there really was an account there, he took the bank pass book and the carbon of the deposit slip over to Hitler himself. As you know, all hell and damnation broke loose."

"All hell is right. Goering has been under house arrest for two weeks without even knowing why. He's not the sort of man who takes something like that lying down. He's been the hero of the German Air Force ever since his World War I days with Richthofen's flying circus and his boys were as hot as three-dollar pistols about it."

Jones smiled. "We've established one fact. For two weeks no one in the German top echelon has been doing one damn thing about the war. God only knows how much that's worth to Uncle Sam. Stopping all those supercharged twenty-four cylinder brains for two weeks right in the middle of the biggest war in history is beyond measurement in money."

Jones paused. "You've done quite a job, John. There's no doubt you are going to get a decoration for it." Jones' smile deepened. "I don't know what the hell the decoration is worth if you can't show it to anybody but at least you can admire it once a year when you open your safe-deposit vault."

"Why all this emphasis on two weeks?"

"The boys finally got wise and Goering is out on the town again. He's mad as hell at Himmler, but not enough to do anything open about it. Himmler is supposed to have asked him what he would have done if it had been the other way around. Claimed he had only done what any other loyal German would have done. Everything is going full blast again now though, they're all back in there fighting the war."

"I better go down and get our thirty thousand bucks back."

"How can you do that?"

Black got to his feet. "At the same time we made out the bank pass book I had the same forger sign Field Marshal Goering's name to a thirty-thousand-dollar, undated check. I'll just date it and cash it. We've had a lot of big bangs for our bucks and now we might as well get the bucks back."

A week later the two men were sitting in the same room. Jones was beaming at Black. "We are still getting reports in about the mess at German topside caused by your bank pass book gimmick. Try to dream up a few more like that. Did you get our thirty thousand dollars back from the Argentine bank?"

Black blushed red with embarrassment. "I got down there and our check bounced like a tennis ball. Field Marshal Goering has already drawn our thirty thousand dollars out."

SEA WATER GOLD

It was a bitter cold night in February, 1897, and two shivering men were sitting in a little house that was perched on the end of a dock that extended out over the Atlantic Ocean. It was off the coast of Rhode Island and the tide was coming in. The two men, both successful businessmen, were Arthur Ryan, a jeweler from Middletown, Connecticut, and Andrew Pierson, the owner of the nation's largest greenhouse. They were huddled around a little potbellied stove in a vain attempt to keep warm.

Ryan blew on his fingers. "If our man was anyone but Prescott Jernegan you certainly wouldn't find me out on the end of this dock. After all, I have known him since he was a boy and he is as close to me as a son. Thanks to me, he graduated from the Newton Theological School and is the Baptist minister in Deland, Florida."

Pierson smiled. "If it wasn't for him I wouldn't be here either. After all, he comes from one of the most reputable families on Martha's Vineyard. He graduated with honors from Brown University, and it isn't everyone who can become an ordained Baptist minister."

Ryan opened the damper of the stove. "Prescott has always been an extraordinarily imaginative person. After all, in my profession as a jeweler I know what everyone else in our profession knows, that there are billions and billions of dollars' worth of pure gold in seawater. It's so diluted that nobody's been able to get it out and make a profit. You can get it out, all right, but it costs more to do it than the value of the gold you get out."

The two men listened to the crunching of the cakes of ice against the piling below them. Ryan looked up. "Are you warm enough to get started?"

There was a large wooden box, lined with zinc, on the floor next to them. Pierson picked it up, uncorked the two flasks of quicksilver on the floor beside him and emptied them into the box. The heavy liquid flashed brightly in the rays of their lanterns.

Ryan attached the hook at the end of the windlass rope to the box. "There is one thing you can say about Prescott, and that is he has done everything in his power to eliminate any chance of fraud from this operation. He made *us* get the box ourselves, and made *us* have it lined with zinc. *We're* going to lower the box into the sea, *we're* going to pull it up, and *we're* going to have the contents tested by a chemist of *our* choice."

Pierson nodded. "The only thing Prescott has done is to take one drop of chemical out of that black bottle he was carrying and drop it into the box.

"What if the stuff he dropped in was gold? Our chemist tomorrow could be finding only what Prescott had dropped in."

Ryan snorted. "Even if that drop was pure gold it wouldn't be nearly enough. He said we are going to get close to five dollars' worth of gold out of this quicksilver when we have it analyzed. It would take an awful lot of those drops to make even one five-dollar gold piece. It's just some sort of chemical that acts as a catalyst. Its action and the current from these batteries isolates the gold." He smiled at his companion. "And after all, what if it doesn't work? All we have lost is a little time and the cost of a wooden box lined with zinc."

Ryan knelt on the floor and attached one electric wire to the zinc lining of the box and the other to the outside of the box. The two men, using the windlass, lowered the box down through a trap door into the frigid waves beneath them. Pierson looked through the trap door and shivered. The tide had risen all right and the dark waters rolled massive and green underneath their dock.

Despite vigorous stoking of the potbellied stove, the two men almost froze in their exposed little cabin. The next morning, numb with cold, they wound up the box with their windlass and took the mercury off to their chemist to be analyzed.

The following day the chemist was ready with his report. "The mercury is just about the same as it was when I sold it to you," he said, "except that it has picked up quite a bit of zinc from somewhere and it contains almost five dollars' worth of gold in solution."

A few minutes later, at his office, Ryan waved the report at his old friend Pierson. "Have you figured this thing out?" he asked. "We lost practically none of the mercury and made five dollars' worth of gold out of ordinary seawater in return for a few cents' worth of electric current." He tried to multiply the figures in his head. "What if we had had five thousand boxes down there and lowered them into the sea with a derrick and a steel cable? With the tide coming in and out all the time, bringing us fresh new water, we'd be clocking off some twenty-five thousand dollars a night."

Pierson was also doing some quick calculating. "Which comes to some nine million a year."

"And there is no law saying you have to limit yourself to five thousand boxes."

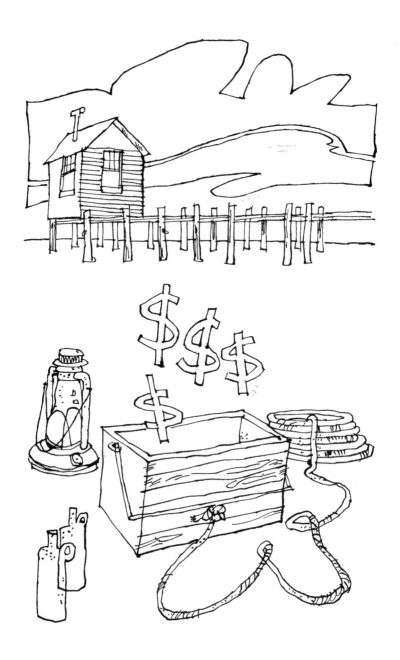

"I'm enough of a businessman to know that if you're going to go into something at all, you might as well do it good idea. You should either not do it at all or do it on the right. There is seldom any use piddling around with a basis which brings you the most profit. The reason I make so much money out of my greenhouse complex is that it is the biggest one in the world. Once I found out that running a small greenhouse was profitable it was just a question of solving the administrative problems involved in having one a hundred times as big."

"What is this all leading up to?"

"I think, to be conservative, we should test this thing three more times on different parts of the Atlantic coast. We'll do it secretly at night so nobody gets wise or curious, and we'll get our mercury from a different source each time and have it analyzed by a different chemist each time. And we'll have it analyzed both before and after we put it in the seawater."

"You're really suspicious, aren't you?"

"No, I am really not. Call it being conservative. I'm convinced we've got something, but in order to do this right, we've got to set up a regular factory to process the sea water on a mass-production basis. That may cost as much as $10 million. That means we will have to bring in our friends and maybe even the general public. When we get into something like that I want to be sure I'm not leading anyone down the primrose path. I want to *know* we've got something."

The next three tests turned out just as successful as the first. The only difference was a slight variation in each case in the percentage of gold obtained.

Jernegan shrugged his shoulders. "It's perfectly obvious there isn't any science to this thing yet. All we know is that, even at this stage of the game, it's profitable. I assume that when we get some good chemists in here, and some top-flight engineers, we can certainly get everything going on a scientific basis."

The Electrolytic Marine Salts Company was formed in the law office of Levi Turner in Portland, Maine, in November, 1897. A group of wealthy businessmen were present, each with a substantial investment and the corporation was capitalized at $10 million with its shares to sell at one dollar a share.

Prescott Jernegan suggested that their first plant be built on Passamaquoddy Bay in Maine, where the forty-foot tides would bring in an unlimited supply of fresh seawater twice a day. His partners agreed and a pilot plant was built on the bay at North Lubec, Maine, to test the process.

A representative of the United States Assay Office in New York City was retained to assay the value of the gold obtained in their first day's operations. It amounted to over $300. Newspapers all over the United States carried the story.

Construction was immediately started on a plant many times as large and hundreds of thousands of dollars' worth of the company's stock was sold to investors.

When the new plant was finally completed the current was switched on and it was put into operation. After a full day's operation not one single gram of gold appeared in the "accumulators." The startled stockholders looked around for Prescott Jernegan and found that he had fled to France with over $100,000 of the company's money. One of the big scandals of the period broke.

Although an enormous amount of work was done on this case by the banks, the police, and the cheated stockholders, it is not yet clear exactly what happened. Evidently Jernegan had a friend named Fisher who was certainly a con man of the most professional ilk. He had some sort of primitive diving suit with its own self-contained air supply, in which he could grope his way under water in the darkness and cold to the zinc-lined wooden boxes under the piers. He would then "salt" them with enough gold to make the process look worthwhile. It was found that during the testing period the proceeds of the stock sales were used by Fisher to buy old gold with which the accumulators were salted.

The unresolved question, of course, was whether Jernegan was equally guilty with his friend Fisher. Although the facts against him are damning, his subsequent history gives some support to the thesis that Jernegan was also an innocent dupe. He sent back over $80,000 of the money he had taken to help pay the debts of the corporation. This he did despite the fact there was no way that the United States Government or the stockholders could have extradited him from France.

The story came full circle some years later when Jernegan himself was defrauded by another seawater gold scheme, which another con man sold him while he was living in England. Jernegan was either one of the cleverest con men in American history or he was one of the most unsophisticated intermediaries that any con man ever used.

In the end, after Jernegan's disappearance and the failure of the accumulators to produce more gold, the newspapers carried a forlorn verse that pretty well summed up the situation.

> "Jernegan, return again.
> Make your plant run again."

THE FRAUDULENT WEAPON

♠

Muldoon was a big, tough, hard drinking, fist fighting Irishman of the "soak your knuckles in brine" school. He was a brilliant, blasphemous, forty-year-old sergeant in the first marine division. He was also the outstanding booby trap expert of the U.S. "Advisors" in Viet Nam. The principal interests he had in life were slant-eyed Viet women and booby traps.

"And what, exactly," he used to roar to his trainees, "is the difference? A woman is a two-legged booby trap with a skirt. A booby trap is a metal woman with an explosive temper and no sense of humor." That one used to lay the boys right out in the aisles. They really needed a little humor now and then because there wasn't one of them who wasn't scared absolutely silly of the deadly booby traps and the dreadful things they had to do with them.

Muldoon laughed his trainees to scorn. "Fine bunch of perfumed granny dishes you are," he shouted. "What exactly in hell is there to be scared of? I have told you muscle heads again and again that there are only *three*

192

basic types of booby traps. The pull type, the push type, and the release type. The pull type goes off when you pull something, the push type goes off when you push something and the release type goes off when you take something off of something. It is just that simple. If you know them, and I mean really know them the way I do, nobody can fool you and you will never get hurt, unless," he smiled waggishly at his students, "the guy who sets the booby trap had more fraud and larceny in his soul than you have." Muldoon winked. "And by the time you graduate from Muldoon University you'll be up over your navel in pure unadulterated fraud. You'll be so loaded with larceny that any honest thought will give you a cold, guilty feeling right in the pit of your stomach."

Muldoon glared at his breathless class. "The way to learn about booby traps is to actually work on them in the field. You have to use the case book system the way the lawyers do." Muldoon's smile was a chilling sight. "Today I have a real live surprise for you jugheads."

The class alerted in fascinated horror.

"Today we are going to leave Quang Ngai, not only because these goddamn Viet women are taking our minds off of our lessons," Muldoon gave his class a pornographic smirk, "including mine, but also you are going to get into the big time. The big, heavy, dangerous, live, explosive big time."

Muldoon paused. "We're going to do a bit of practicing on a real, honest-to-God live mine field outside Quang Ngai. It has been untouched and roped-off ever since we bombed the Viet Cong out of here. So all we have to do is roll up our sleeves, get our wills all made out, and get to work—dirty, fraudulent work."

Before the members of his class had time to do more than exchange horrified glances, Muldoon herded them into an army bus and they found themselves bouncing along the rough Viet Namese road. Muldoon smiled back with grim satisfaction at the tense, white, faces around him. Obviously the thought of working on the real thing was getting his boys right smack in the pits of their stomachs. Right exactly where it did the most good. They were gibbering back there like a bunch of Barbary apes.

Muldoon's smile broadened as he watched one recruit try to light a cigarette. His match went out four times before he lit the filter end by mistake. It smelled as if his underwear was on fire but he kept on blowing out the greenish smoke. Muldoon shook his head. Nothing scared the hell out of a man more than fear.

The mine field turned out to be a square mile of jungle interspersed with tiny clearings in which many small buildings were hidden from overhead view by the overhanging trees. Much of the area was fire-blackened, particularly around the many tunnel entrances.

The trainees looked around them with apprehensive eyes. Muldoon grinned appreciatively. They didn't like those craters all around them. Each crater was the spot where a you-know-what had exploded and had blown the legs right smack off of somebody.

The recruits stood motionless in a dense, scared group. Directly in front of them was one of the big wooden signboards that surrounded the area. Their warning was in both English and Viet:

EXTREME DANGER—LAND MINE FIELD
KEEP AWAY—EXTREME DANGER

Muldoon gave his students time to gawk at the terrain and at the signs and then got everyone's attention by assembling a mine detector.

Muldoon, deliberate and cautious as a wolf, moved the disc out at the end of its long pole over a piece of bare ground. Suddenly the indicator needle gave a convulsive jerk. The whole class jerked with it. Something deadly and terrible lay buried there out of sight under the turf.

Muldoon put down the mine detector and dropped to his knees. He started to dig, inch by inch. He uncovered the edge of the mine and dug in cautiously to the naked fuse. He started to unscrew it and then looked up with a smile. His students stood transfixed. Finally, with a triumphant gesture, Muldoon held up the unscrewed fuse. He reached down and, ignoring the collective gasp of horror from the class, picked up the deadly mine and heaved it into the ditch. Three members of the class recoiled precipitately into the ditch behind them and fell in the slime up to their necks.

Muldoon quickly located another mine and went through the whole process of removing the fuse in exactly the same way. Then he stood up and pointed to the least scared-looking student in the class. "OK, Jones, you tell me what to do next."

Jones stepped briskly forward. His voice was confident. "Just pick it up," he said, "and throw it into the ditch the way you did the other one."

Muldoon gave Jones a look of deep pity. Then he delicately lowered a loop of rope so that it circled the mine, not quite touching it. He motioned the class to follow him and they all moved off to the end of the rope— about one hundred feet. Muldoon gave the rope a jerk. There was a deafening explosion and a huge orange flash. Sand and rubble spouted up in the air like a volcanic eruption.

Muldoon wheeled and ·pointed to Jones. "You are lying there on the ground," he said, "with both of your legs blown off. The Cong who set that mine was a lot smarter than you, Jones. He planted two booby traps, one positioned on top of the other. Even though I had the fuse removed out of the top one, if I picked it up the movement would have set off the bottom one. It had a *release* type fuse."

Jones nodded numbly.

The class was so badly frightened by this time they could hardly speak, but their lesson had only started. Muldoon seemed to know all the tricks of the trade and every trick he showed them bleached their faces a shade whiter.

Finally they came to a house on the edge of the warning area. It was surrounded by concrete gun emplacements. Muldoon hooted with joy. "Now hear this," he shouted. "The battle of Quang Ngai went over this section so fast everything is still just the way the Cong left it." He pointed. "I know damn well that house is booby trapped. Why? I just know, that's all." He rubbed his hands together gleefully. "Let's go in and work out on it."

Walking cautiously as if treading on eggs, the class followed its electronic mine detector in single file around the front of the house. As they rounded the corner a shout from Muldoon halted them in their tracks. He was pointing to a wire hanging from the roof along the side of the building. "There is a perfect storybook trap for jugheads like you," he yelled. He waited until everyone was around him and then started his lecture.

"Suppose," he said, "you captured a layout like this and you see a messy looking wire hanging down like that. It isn't really important except from a tidiness standpoint. You don't have to clean that up until you've done everything else. When you've got the house all cleaned up and tickety boo, everyone moves in and settles down happy as a bunch of clams. Finally one of those 'ship-shape' characters comes along, decides that wire looks untidy, and gives it a yank. It is a pull type booby trap so the whole house and everyone in it gets blown sky high."

Muldoon thrust his chin out at his class. "Now how would you children go about getting that wire down? How about you, Jones?"

Jones smiled feebly. "After that last decision I would just leave it up there. To hell with it."

Muldoon shoved his fist through every suggestion anyone made. He glared at his class disapprovingly. "There is just one way to do it," he explained at last. "First you get yourself safely stashed away in that machine gun emplacement. It's solid concrete and its walls are a foot thick. Then you reach over with a long pole with a wire hook on the end and give the hanging wire a good pull. When the booby trap goes off, the pieces may rattle all around you but you're safe as in a church in your concrete emplacement."

It was painfully clear to the members of his class that Muldoon had a magic sixth sense about booby traps. They all wished they had it too. Everything he showed them only scared them more.

There was very little room in the machine gun emplacement so Muldoon made everyone get back one hundred and fifty feet while he lowered himself into the safety of its solid concrete walls. He reached out with his long pole, hooked the wire, and jerked it. There was a gigantic orange flash and a thunderous roar as the mine went off. The concussion hit the members of the horrified class with a shock wave that flattened them prone on the turf.

After they recovered enough to open their eyes and scramble to their feet, they stared at each other like a flock of terrified sheep. That was no land mine. It sounded and looked like a ton of nitro-starch. They stared at the partially demolished house. The mine had exploded right under Muldoon's machine gun emplacement. There was nothing left there but a black smoldering hole in the ground. Then their eyes shifted to an object about fifty feet to one side. It looked like a bundle of burning rags. Muldoon University needed a new president.

THE FRAUDULENT BIRTHDAY

♠

Goddard Stone glanced at the girl out of the corners of his eyes. She was driving the car along as if nothing unpleasant had ever happened between them. The damnedest switch he had ever seen. But then who the hell could ever explain women? Stone smiled grimly. And if *he* couldn't explain them, exactly who in hell could? He leaned back in the comfortable seat. So here they were, going out to her family's house again, after hours. He looked at Amassa appreciatively. Anyone who had a daughter like Amassa was really asking for something when they left her alone in a great big house like that. Again the grim smile. That was a situation he could certainly take care of all right. And in fact had, many times.

Amassa Stewart looked over at him with a bright smile. "Happy birthday, darling," she said.

Stone grinned. So that was it. Just boiled down to one of those ways all women had for getting back to first base when they found the big bust-up scene didn't get them what they wanted. Women, even the real dishes like

Amassa, were just as predictable as a bunch of cows in a field. He glanced over at her. She certainly looked a hell of a lot different now than she had during that bust-up scene. "You are a fraud," she had screamed at him. "A fraud, fraud, fraud. You cheat women just exactly the way a confidence man cheats with money." She had burst into tears. "And that's much worse because women are more sensitive and you really injure them."

Stone's lips turned down at the corners. Exactly what in hell use was there being a bachelor if you were expected to marry every girl you climbed into bed with. It was a sort of game, really. They wanted to obligate you into marrying them and you wanted to roll them in the hay and go on to someone else. It was a game, really, like football. Amassa had been perfectly right about that part. What Amassa had forgotten was that people did get hurt in football. It never stopped the game though, except for the player who got the broken leg.

Stone looked at Amassa ruefully. "When you're fifty-five years old you try to forget your birthdays," he said.

She smiled. "Well, I haven't forgotten this one. I'll bet you've already guessed what's going to happen."

Stone grinned. He had guessed all right. It was nice to see that their feud was over. As they used to say in the Army, Amassa was a damned good officer's mount and he didn't want to lose her.

They went into the big dark house and closed the door. "I'm going to leave the lights out," she whispered. "I don't think we'll need them." He turned and grasped her head roughly between his hands. They needed the lights about as much as they needed muscular dystrophy. He kissed her hard on the lips.

Amassa pushed him gently away. "All that can wait," she whispered, "until I can go up stairs and get into something a little more sensible. You go into the living room to wait and I'll be right down."

Stone allowed himself to be pushed into the living room. He knew what she meant all right by "more sensible." She was going to come down the way she always had before, without one single stitch on. Stone heard her moving around in the bedroom over his head. It was one of the things that had intrigued him most about Amassa, really. The tremendous difference between her prim demeanor in the office and the way she acted here in her own house when her family was out of town. It was exciting, all right, but it was also extremely practical. It meant no one in his office had the slightest idea there was anything intimate between them.

Stone took off his coat and started to unfasten his tie. High time he got into something more sensible himself.

A few seconds later all of Stone's clothes were draped over a chair and he was taking off his socks. He shivered slightly. Would have to remind Amassa all over again to put up the thermostat before he came over. Up to about 80. He heard Amassa coming down the stairs and turned expectantly.

"Happy Birthday," she cried. And suddenly he heard many men's and women's voices singing: "Happy birthday to you. Happy birthday to you. Happy birthday, Mister Stone. Happy birthday to you."

The dining room doors flew open and the lights flashed on. As Goddard dived frantically for his underwear he saw the whole staff of his office, their glasses held high in a toast, staring at him in open-mouthed amazement.

FINALLY THE PERFECT MURDER

♠

The Prosecuting Attorney glared at Ishmael. His voice had a loud confident ring. "Where were you at three o'clock in the afternoon of May the fourteenth of this year?"

Ishmael looked at him amiably. "At just that time I was extremely busy. I was chopping Leonora Snow's head off with my Boy Scout hatchet. Also I was fighting off my brother who was trying, for some reason, to stop me."

There was a tremendous flurry in the jury box and in the press section. All the newsmen started writing frantically and handing notes to little messenger boys.

The members of the jury looked absolutely flabbergasted. They were sitting there with their mouths wide open staring at the defendant and his brother. It was the murder trial of the century. The jury foreman, a formidable-looking woman of about fifty, was glaring at Ishmael. What an absolutely bestial monster, she thought. There is one monster that *must* end up in the electric chair. He has *got* to end up there for the good of society.

Ishmael glared right back at her. Maybe he *was* a monster but at least, he thought with satisfaction, he was an orderly one. He smiled amiably at the jury foreman. He would like to drive his Boy Scout hatchet right smack into the back of her neck. By God, that would make the blood fly.

Even Judge Throckmorton, who had always been famous for his imperturbability, had a startled, unjudicial expression on his face. He tried manfully, but even he couldn't keep the distaste completely off his face when he looked at Ishmael.

The Prosecutor's façade of confidence vanished and his mouth was also hanging open. Finally he found his voice. "You admit, then, to the jury," he stammered, "that you murdered Leonora Snow?"

Ishmael's black eyes twinkled with amusement. He laughed jovially. "Of course I murdered her. That's why I took my hatchet along. I had it hidden under my coat."

There was a quick rustle of horror which swept over the huge courtroom like an ocean wave. Hundreds of pairs of eyes were looking at Ishmael accusingly; he smiled and acknowledged the looks as if he were being applauded.

The Prosecuting Attorney was incredulous. "You mean that you admit to the jury that you actually premeditated this murder and actually took your hatchet in under your coat to kill Leonora Snow?"

Ishmael looked indignantly at the Prosecuting Attorney. "Certainly, I premeditated it. Do you think I'm the sort of person who goes around carrying a carefully sharpened hatchet under his coat for no reason at all? I had a terrible time hiding the hatchet so Joe wouldn't see it when we were walking over to her house together."

"Did Joe know that you were going to kill Miss Snow?"

"No, he didn't. In fact, when I took out the hatchet and started working her over with it, Joe did his very best to pull me away. Of course, I'm quite a bit stronger than he is, so he just held me up for a few seconds. I had to slap the hell out of him to quiet him down. He was really wrought up about it, though, and after she was dead he picked up the telephone and called the police. He's always meddling in my affairs."

A murmur of laughter swept over the courtroom and was quickly extinguished by Judge Throckmorton.

The Prosecutor was beginning to look relieved. "Exactly why did you murder Miss Snow?"

"It was because she laughed at me. She thought it was funny the way Joe and I were always together. Said it made her feel funny about me. I gave her my love and admiration and she only laughed."

"Do you think that was enough excuse to justify your barbarously chopping up and killing an innocent eighteen-year-old girl?"

"Yes, I do, or I wouldn't have done it. She caused me much more pain than I caused her. Getting killed with a nice sharp hatchet was too good for Leonora."

Again that swift murmur fled over the courtroom and this time the Judge banged his gavel on the desk. "If there is any further demonstration of any kind whatsoever I will order the Bailiff to clear the courtroom." Instantly there was dead silence.

The court reporter was scribbling furiously in his little notebook and the jurors were whispering to each other as they filed out to the jury room to reach a verdict.

In a record seven minutes the jurors filed back into the jury box. The foreman stood up. Her attitude was one of deep satisfaction. "The Jury finds the defendant guilty of murder in the first degree without recommendation of mercy."

The Judge looked at Ishmael coldly. "You have heard the verdict. Have you anything to say before I pass sentence on you?"

"Yes, I have," Ishmael's voice seemed to carry an undercurrent of amusement. "I realize, Your Honor, that in this state when the jury makes finding of first degree murder without recommendation of mercy, a sentence of death by electrocution is mandatory. I submit, Your Honor, the perfectly obvious fact that this sentence cannot legally be carried out in my case. It is obviously and completely impossible for the state to electrocute me without killing an innocent person who had nothing at all to do with the crime and, in fact, tried his desperate best to stop it. I have a certificate here signed by each member of a consultation of the top surgeons of this city. It states that if I die this will, within a few hours, cause the death of my Siamese-twin brother, Joe. We have a common liver, Your Honor, and other organs as well, and we cannot surgically be separated. Or, I can say, we would have been long since. By carrying out a death sentence against me this state would be murdering a completely innocent man. Such an action would be a violation of both the State and the Federal Constitutions and could therefore not be legally carried out.

"My Siamese-twin brother Joe's attorneys are now in the process of preparing a habeas corpus and a request for an injunction which will prevent him from being further detained or molested in any way by the authorities. I can not be electrocuted or even detained or incarcerated without Joe's being forcibly deprived of his Constitutional freedoms. I see his lawyer coming up the central aisle now, Your Honor, with a piece of paper in his hand. It gives me great pleasure at this time to bid you and the delightful members of your jury a merry Christmas and a happy New Year."

VACATION IN ATLANTIC CITY

♠

David Climo, who was usually a very successful and competent confidence man, eventually found out, as most of them do, that he had to go on the lam. He had to get out of his home city of Chicago fast! One of his plots, involving a young Chicago businessman named Joseph Patrick McGinley, had backfired on him. An attractive young man with lots on the ball, McGinley had been completely outraged when he found that his "friend" David Climo was a cheap confidence man who had lost him a very substantial amount of money on a phony stock racket.

Joseph McGinley turned over some of Climo's letters to the United States mail fraud authorities and called in the FBI and the Chicago police. A man with strong political connections, he used them all in a vengeful attempt to catch Climo and put him in jail.

After two or three exceedingly narrow escapes, Climo, in desperation, fled Chicago and went down to Atlantic City to give his pursuers a chance to cool off. He registered at one of the least conspicuous hotels, the Galen Hall Hotel, under the name of Tom Brady.

Things got pretty boring pretty fast for the newly named "Tom Brady," who had always been a generous contributor to the fast night life of Chicago. The Galen Hall Hotel was designed largely for old ladies who came to take the baths and medicinal treatments and was, "Brady" decided, just about as exciting as a mashed potato sandwich.

"Brady" walked down to the beach every morning in his bathing suit, stayed in an inconspicuous place under the edge of the boardwalk where nobody would be likely to recognize him, and gradually got sunburned and bored and frustrated. He took the turkish baths at Galen Hall, played pool with the turkish bath attendant and went through the various exercise routines. If he couldn't somehow find some female companionship, he decided, he was going to blow his stack like an old Civil War locomotive.

"Brady" looked around the hotel dining room that evening with distaste. It was filled mostly with prim old ladies who looked as if they might be wearing sneakers. A few of them had moth-eaten, subdued-looking husbands. There seemed to be just one eligible woman in the whole damned hotel. He stared across the dining room at her. She was certainly in the wrong place. She seemed to be about thirty years old, obviously a very reserved and conservative type. She certainly had that appearance of gentility that always seemed to appeal to him for some reason. She was attractive-looking, too, good bone structure, with high cheekbones and an extremely usable figure. That air of reserve and gentility was what really got him though. It would certainly be fun to ruffle that up and to roll her around in bed a bit.

"Brady" looked up from his menu and found that she was looking at him. She did not drop her eyes the way most girls would have. She looked at him quietly for a moment as if he was part of the scenery and then her eyes wandered off to examine the other people in the room. "Brady" felt a slight sense of pique. She certainly didn't

seem to pay any more attention to him than to anyone else. Maybe she had him junked in with the rest of the creeps in the room—the sneaker brigade. One skill every confidence man has is his ability to strike up an acquaintance. An hour later "Brady" and the woman were rolling down the boardwalk in a wheel chair, one of those with the canopy and the fringe on top. "Brady" mentally summarized what he had already learned. Her name was Beatrice Franklin. She came from a small town, Lotis, Pennsylvania. She had been very unhappily married to someone who had treated her badly and she was just getting over the shock. That, he thought, was where he came in. He would play the role of the one who helped her forget.

"Brady" started mentally undressing her and glanced away quickly as she looked up at him. One had to creep along pretty slowly with something like this. She certainly wasn't just any old bag you would roll over in the hay like a sack of potatoes. He smiled happily to himself. There was one thing every con man had to know, and he knew it—in each particular case, do you use the hard sell or the soft sell? He looked down at her again. This was obviously the soft-sell type. He had to appear to be retreating while he was advancing. Just the same as old Christopher Columbus. When he wanted to go East, he sailed West.

Two days later they were having dinner together. She looked radiantly at him across the table. "I've never been so happy before in my life," she said. "It's never ever been like this before with me."

"Brady" smiled back at her. It had taken a couple of slow days all right. The soft sell was always a slow sell, but this time it turned out to be worth every minute of it. This was no ordinary roll in the hay. Beatrice was really something. If he was the marrying type this would be what he really wanted. It looked as though there might be some truth in the old saying, "thoroughbred mares are the most passionate." "Brady" looked at her uneasily. There was one thing wrong with it, though. Beatrice wasn't just playing pinochle, the way he was. She was playing for keeps. Being a con man never went too well with being married, and it sure wouldn't in this case.

"Brady" sat thinking. He had obviously let things go too far. If she wasn't pregnant by this time he was a monkey's uncle. If he didn't watch out he was going to have her wrapped around his neck like a goddamned octopus. It was certainly high time he unloaded her on someone else. He smiled at her across the table. But who and how? He sat thinking. It might be fun to give one of his enemies a real ride on this situation—something that would embarrass the bejesus out of him before it all got straightened out.

Suddenly "Brady" sat bolt upright. Beatrice looked at him startled. "It's nothing," he said lamely, "just a couple of things I had forgotten, business affairs." He signaled the waiter for their check. That was the fellow all right, Joseph Patrick McGinley, the son of a bitch who had sicked everyone on him. Fouled him up and had him hiding down here in Atlantic City, hiding from the Post Office inspectors and the FBI. That was the man all right. He'd have a little fun with McGinley.

"Brady" reached over and took his companion's hand. "I have a terrible confession to make," he said.

She smiled up at him. "You could tell me just about anything and make me like it."

He squeezed her hand. "My name isn't Tom Brady." She looked up at him startled. "It is Joseph Patrick McGinley, and I am from Chicago. I came down here on a special job for Central Intelligence. I had to use a phony name for the job and it's been killing me ever since I met you. This has been the most wonderful week of my life. Although it's a gross violation of security to tell you, I just couldn't stand your not knowing. If you're a Russian agent I am finished."

He stared at her. "It is not the name I am worried about, though, darling. That's just government business, very secret business. It's that tomorrow I have to fly abroad for six months on a mission. You can guess the sort of mission it is. And during that period I am not even going to be able to write to you. If anyone even suspected you knew my name I would be in the most serious trouble imaginable. After six months, though, I will be back in the United States and everything will be all right. We can get married."

Even the hardened sensibilities of "Tom Brady" were shaken by their tearful farewell the next afternoon. Beatrice smiled at him through her tears. "I am going to be thinking and dreaming of you, and marking the days off on my calendar like a convict. If you don't call me in six months to the day I will call you, Joseph Patrick McGinley, and fly to Chicago to share your bed and board!"

Two months later "Tom Brady" was again David Climo. He was reading the *Chicago Tribune* on the porch of his Chicago penthouse apartment. Suddenly he sat bolt upright in his chair. The headline was screaming at him . . . "PENNSYLVANIA HEIRESS."

"Pennsylvania heiress killed in airplane wreck last week leaves major fortune to Chicago businessman. Beatrice Franklin, in a stunning surprise to her own relatives, left the bulk of her twenty-million-dollar steel fortune to Joseph Patrick McGinley, a prominent socialite and businessman of this city, 'for reasons only he and I understand.' "

THE FRAUD ON THE ROAD

♠

Alex Lee shifted the jeep out of four-wheel drive and coasted down the crooked, narrow street that the English-man humorously called the "Avenue of the United Nations." As they drove into the little Moroccan village the low adobe houses blotted out the vast panorama of the snow-capped Atlas Mountains to their right—the "Idraren Draren," the "Mountains of Mountains," of the Arab legends—the mountains where El Ates was waiting.

"Stop!" It was the Turk's deep voice from the back seat. Alex jerked his lanky frame to attention and pulled on the brake. They stopped right in front of the "Le Brave Spahi." The three of them, the Englishman, the Turk, and the German, got out and, without a backward glance at him, stalked into Casbah-Djelfa's only bar.

Alex sighed—couldn't very well blame them; who the devil was he? Even as he turned off the motor and radio transmitter, he could hear the tremendous din inside the barracks-like structure, full of drunks and madmen as usual; the carefully decanted scum of the world, French-men, Arabs, Berbers, and Englishmen, the worst of every color, race, and creed. They were the soldiers and camp followers of France's most exposed outpost, the one trying to contain the revolutionist, El Ates.

It was not the happiest place, Alex bitterly realized, for an American who should have been back working in his father's insurance business. He had wanted a change when he left Cleveland, something different and romantic. He had certainly got the change part. The first week was enough to show him he hated it. Three more years to go on his enlistment—if he didn't go mad first.

He entered the "oasis." Every table except one was crowded and there were three lines of jostling customers at the bar. A few were even doing their drinking on the floor.

Alex's sad, grey eyes swept the room. Right near the entrance, startlingly empty in the most crowded part of all, was the famous table, with even a respectful circle of empty floor space around it and, of course, the three empty chairs. It had no "reserved" sign—everyone knew—and looked as if the riffraff thought it was radio-active.

There was the same hush there always was when they came in—the three toughest of the Spahis' tough—so inseparable, so constantly together that what else could they be called in an organization as typically French as the Spahis but "Les Trois Mousquetaires." There was Monsieur Shaw, the lanky young Englishman who looked like the second son of some English lord, and probably was. He usually rode in the front seat of the jeep with Alex.

Then there was Monsieur Dosdogru, the burly Turk, who never seemed to exercise but he had laughingly pinned the Spahi's wrestling champion flat on the dance floor the week before when he had got out of hand. Finally, Monsieur Von Estorff, the German with the thin white scar on his left cheek.

Alex's envious eyes followed them. Those were not the names they called each other, though. Never, Alex thought wistfully, had there been a more envied aristocracy anywhere than among his jeepmates—and it was deserved—an aristocracy of toughness, military skill, and deep, long friendship. Stuck in this out-of-the-way hole, he would have given his very life to be part of it. He despairingly needed it—a man could die of boredom. It was too much, he thought bitterly, to spend most of every day in an exclusive club and not be a member of it. He was just their driver.

Unconsciously, without meaning to exclude him, they exulted in their friendship with their tough, masculine humor—an insulting freedom they had with each other which they tolerated from no one else. Their names for each other were part of it. They very formally called him "Monsieur Lee," but Dosdogru, the Turk, a Moslem to whom pigs were unclean animals, was never referred to by any other name than "Pig." It was a standing joke among the three of them, but Alex remembered the terrible beating they gave the Russian, Ivan Novokoff, right in this room, when *he* dared call the Turk "Pig."

The German, a former Reichswehr officer who had been broken and hounded out of Germany by Hitler, was of course called "Adolf" by the other two—but by no one else. The Englishman, whose loyalty to the British Royal Family was part of his background, was always called "Queen Elizabeth" or just plain "Lizzie."

Alex stood miserably at the door as the three stalked over to their table. The frantic waiter just barely made it and the three pernods were safely on the table when they arrived, their green surfaces still trembling.

This was the loneliest part of the day for Alex, the moment he passed by their table as they were sitting down—passed by them to join the motley crowd of drunks at the bar—his echelon. This was the time of day he had the most wretched homesickness for Cleveland, regrets about his senseless fight with his father, and his ridiculous gesture, running off and joining the Spahis. He would have joined the Foreign Legion if it hadn't sounded too corny, too much like a cheap dime novel. If he had known then what he knew now about the Spahis, he would have taken his chances with the Mau Maus.

Alex was deathly sick of speaking French and Arabic, of being dirty, and of wearing a uniform that didn't fit. He was sick of the knot that tied itself in his stomach when he thought of the bodies of the four Spahis they had found yesterday near their demolished jeep. "Men can't die more painfully than that," the Englishman had said. Even the Turk's face had been ashen. "El Ates' work," he had muttered.

Alex was also sick of having absolutely nothing to do but stand jammed in between smelly, drunken bodies at the bar. He wondered what he would be like in three years. He had a pretty clear choice—become like one of these around the bar—blow his stack—or go queer because there was no one to talk to. He looked back at the table. They weren't impolite or rude, the three of them; they just didn't know he existed. Why should they? He was only their jeep driver.

Their table was an oasis—an oasis where English was spoken instead of patois French, where the conversation was intelligent and educated and humorous, with the kind of humor they had back home. He looked around him. An oasis where no one got drunk, only one pernod, perhaps two. Their uniforms fitted, and they looked and acted like soldiers, and they were. Alex thought of the stories that were told about them. But, as was customary in the Spahis, the "Trois Mousquetaires" rarely discussed their past, except to admit they had known each other as students at Oxford.

They were getting up. The waiter was beaming at the

size of his tip. There, they were beckoning to him. Alex jumped like a school boy and put his half-finished pernod on the counter. As he turned to go, a wild drunken fight broke out over the remains of his drink. He heard a crash of glass and a furious curse behind him.

♠

  It was mid-afternoon and Alex was squinting his eyes against the sun as they bounced along the Avenue of the United Nations. "What does the name El Ates mean?" he asked respectfully. "It must be Arabic, but I don't recognize it."

  "You speak beautiful Arabic, Monsieur Lee," the Turk answered courteously from the back seat. "*Ates* means 'the fire' in Turkish."

  The German grunted. "One of his Moslem mullahs, who came from your country, 'Pig,' gave him that name because of what he does to the foreigners he captures."

  Alex felt the knot in his stomach again. "He must be a sadist," he said, hoping he was not intruding too much in their conversation. "Wouldn't it be less trouble to shoot them?"

  The Englishman's voice was even quieter than usual. "El Ates may be sadistic but he is also very intelligent. He is following a formula. He wants the French out of North Africa. If he shoots one Frenchman, that is only one less. If he burns him at the stake and publicizes the fact, twenty French families will leave Morocco forever."

  The Turk's deep rumble came from the back seat. "It certainly works around here, 'Lizzie.' The Spahis are the only foreigners left."

  The German grunted. "If we don't catch him pretty quick, he'll scare everyone out of North Africa."

  "How can we search any harder? Besides," the Turk laughed, "if El Ates really has those new Russian command cars, who is hunting who, anyway? He could drive down to Casbah-Djelfa and capture our fort, dirty uniforms, pernod, obsolete bold-action rifles, and all. Did you look at that hole in the wrecked jeep yesterday? I still think it was hit by a recoil-less seventy-five millimeter cannon." There was an uncomfortable silence. The German lit up a cigarette. "If he took Casbah-Djelfa he'd have enough prisoners for the biggest fire of his career."

"We certainly haven't got anything heavy enough to lick seventy-five millimeter recoil-less cannon," said the Englishman, "until our own tanks come—and that may be a week." He banged the side of the jeep. "Rattling along in this bucket, we're just like three mice out on reconnaissance to find the cat."

Alex shifted viciously into high. He wasn't even the fourth mouse.

The jeep started to labor and Alex shifted back into second. They were entering the first of the passes in the foothills of the "Mountains of Mountains." Two-hundred-foot cliffs hung over them on each side of the narrow road. Alex felt exposed. There was always the chance that a Berber marksman was crouched down behind one of those stubby little bushes. Better step on it a little.

He rounded the next corner too fast and Alex felt every nerve in his body leap. "Jesus," shouted the Englishman. "Allah," yelled the Turk. "Mother of God," muttered the German. Alex slammed on the brakes. Fifty yards ahead the road was blocked by a monstrous armored car that looked like a gigantic armored beetle—and another behind that—and another, and another. The cannon on the first was leveled right at them, its black mouth wide open, ready to speak. Alex could see the Berber gunner staring at them. His hand was on the lanyard.

"Turn around," yelled the Englishman. "Back up,"

shouted the German. "We'll die fighting," whispered the Turk.

Someone ahead of them shouted a command in Arabic and Alex found himself frantically waving his white handkerchief. "What the hell are you doing?" shouted the Turk. "Shut up!" Alex snapped. He was shocked at the decisiveness in his voice. "We've got to bluff. Our only chance. Can blow us to smithereens. Even if we could turn, those armored cars are much faster than this ash can."

Alex put the jeep in gear and, still waving the handkerchief, moved slowly forward. His stomach crawled as the mouth of the cannon depressed to keep them in range. He heard another shouted order and saw the gunner take his hand off the lanyard. They had lost all chance for a merciful death now. He yelled furiously at his three startled companions.

"Put those guns down. Got to bluff it, I tell you." He drew up in front of the armored car that looked as big as a house. The recoil-less cannon had depressed its aim and was staring black-mouthed right into their windshield, ten feet away. "Allah could have given me a better death," muttered the Turk. Alex opened the door and, still waving his handkerchief, got out and saluted. "I am a herald," he said in Arabic, "from General Secherrez with a message to His Excellency the Kaid El Ates. Please take us to him."

A powerfully built Berber officer wearing a Spahi fatigue outfit too small for him got out of the armored car. "Throw your guns on the ground," he ordered. Alex halted the Turk's growl almost before it started. "Get out and throw them down," he snapped. He took his automatic out of his holster and tossed it on the road. His three companions glared at him a moment and then sullenly threw down their guns. A turbaned soldier stepped nervously forward and collected them.

The officer searched them for weapons and smiled.

"His Excellency, the Kaid El Ates, is very happy to have prisoners. He uses them to divert his soldiers."

"But we come under a flag of truce, we're not prisoners," protested Alex.

"You will please maintain silence." Alex felt his companions staring at him. God, how they must hate him—and they would hate him more later.

They had gone only a few steps when Alex saw the door of the last armored car open. A tall, turbaned figure in a flowing black galibesh got out. Instantly every slouching, ragged tribesman snapped to attention. For the first time, Alex thought, they looked like soldiers.

There was the rumble of a deep voice. "What do we have here?" Alex recognized El Ates from his pictures—the thin, cruel face with its vulture nose, much lighter than his almost-black tribesmen, the large, intelligent yellow eyes, the compressed straight mouth.

Their guard stiffened to attention and saluted. "Prisoners, Your Excellency." He grinned. "Firewood." The Kaid's thin smile brought the knot back into Alex's stomach. "Not prisoners, Your Excellency. We are heralds under a flag of truce bringing a message to Your Excellency from General Secherrez."

The thin smile vanished. "Where is the message?" he demanded. Alex suddenly felt cold.

"It's a verbal message, Your Excellency."

The yellow eyes widened with astonishment. "A *verbal* message?" His smile came back. "And you expect me to believe a fraud like that?"

Alex felt the words tumbling out as if someone else were saying them. "There was no time for anything else, Your Excellency. A wireless message came in saying you were moving down the Draren Road in full force with seven armored cars. General Secherrez is this minute coming up to meet you with ten General Sherman tanks. Any one of them could defeat your whole force."

El Ates' smile vanished and his mouth opened, but Alex did not stop. "General Secherrez knows you cannot turn around on this narrow road. He knows Your Excellency is trapped. He wants to prevent bloodshed and is willing to give Your Excellency honorable surrender terms." Alex paused. "Our General is a great admirer of Your Excellency's military ability and knows it is only by good fortune that he has you in his power. He is willing to discuss terms in a meeting with you halfway between our forces. If you cannot agree on terms the battle can proceed."

The great yellow eyes focused on his and stared. Alex hoped the hammering of his heart did not show. The Kaid's smile came back. "You are very clever. How do I know you are not lying?" He paused. "I have some specialists who can find out."

"There is not time for that, Your Excellency. The fact I am not lying is proved by my driving up to seven armored cars in a jeep."

The Kaid laughed scornfully. "Why did General Secherrez not send an *officer* with his verbal message? Does he feel that in dealing with an inferior like El Ates, only a common soldier is necessary?"

Alex felt himself grow red. "He asked for volunteers, Your Excellency. None of the Spahis officers dared come." He looked down at the ground. "I am ashamed to say our officers are—afraid of Your Excellency." There was a roar of laughter and the tension disappeared. Even El Ates smiled absently. Alex could see he was thinking of something else, probably some refinement of torture for them.

"Ten Sherman tanks, you say?"

"Yes, Your Excellency, plus, of course, the regular infantry stationed at Casbah-Djelfa."

The yellow eyes stared at him for a full minute without blinking. Alex stared back. He must be firm but not arrogant enough to give offense.

"I will accept your General's suggestion that we confer. My respect for him is as high as his for me, and I also wish to shed no blood unnecessarily." He lowered his voice. "The meeting must, of course, be a formal one conducted with respect and honor to both commanders." He paused. "A formal dinner meeting at, say, eight o'clock tonight. Will that be satisfactory?"

His relief was so great that Alex found himself physically unable to answer. He was deathly afraid his voice would betray him. He bowed respectfully and put his hand over his heart in the Arab manner. The gesture seemed to steady him.

"I am sure it will be. I suggest, Your Excellency, that both Your Excellency and my General send officers to work out the details of the meeting. They could meet in an hour at the river crossing if Your Excellency wishes." He knew now what the Kaid would say.

Alex was sure he saw a spark of triumph in the cold, yellow eyes, but it vanished instantly. "Go tell your General that will be satisfactory—only make it two hours." Alex nodded his head—he had expected it to be three.

At a signal from the Kaid twenty tribesmen upended the jeep, turned it half a revolution and lowered it facing the other way. As they rounded the bend Alex could hear shovels digging and gears grinding.

"Listen. They are mining the road," said the Turk. "Also," chuckled the German, "hear the reverse gears— they can't turn—they are backing into the mountains."

"There is a turnaround about five miles back," laughed the Englishman. "If they can make it they will be saved from our non-existent tanks." He picked up the phone, turned on the scrambler, and gave the fort a complete account of what had happened. He gave Alex full credit for everything. He hung up. "You were very clever, Mr. Lee." Alex was not surprised at the lack of real enthusiasm in his voice—after all, he had saved their lives, saved them from much worse than death, and in doing so had humiliated them.

"You certainly were, Mr. Lee," said the Turk.

"I've never seen anyone think faster, Mr. Lee," said the German.

Alex looked straight ahead. He laughed deprecatingly. "I didn't do a thing. The three of you were so calm it carried the bluff off. El Ates just chickened out, that's all."

He felt the Englishman looking at him. "What do you mean, chickened out?"

"In America, we call a coward a 'chicken.'"

The Englishman grunted and lit a cigarette. Alex noticed he offered one to everyone but him. "American slang is so expressive—chicken." The Englishman lingered over the word as if he were tasting its flavor— "chicken." He pulled down the back of the seat and sat on it, facing the other way, toward his two friends. The jeep was so noisy Alex could only hear a word here and there—they were purposely excluding him from their conversation.

As they jolted up the crooked twisting "Avenue of the United Nations" they were about to pass "Le Brave Spahi" when the Englishman raised his hand. "Stop," he ordered curtly.

Alex pulled on the brake. "Les Trois Mousquetaires" climbed out and without a backward glance, stalked into the bistro. Alex shut off the ignition, put the key in his pocket, and snapped off the radio. He arrived at the door just in time for their grand entrance.

He saw that "Le Brave Spahi" was jammed with the usual roaring mob of drunken soldiers, Berbers, entertainers, thieves, and beggars. Every table and chair was so overoccupied that there were three jostling lines of customers at the bar with a few even doing their drinking on the floor.

Right near the entrance, startlingly empty, was the table. Never, Alex thought, had it looked so arrogant—a powerful fortress proudly holding the riffraff at bay, even when its defenders were absent. There was the usual hush when they came in, not a silence, but a diminution of the clamor, a little sharper note to the buzz. The three paid not the slightest attention. The frantic waiter just barely made it, three light green pernods were safely on the table when they arrived, their surfaces still trembling.

Alex went miserably past them as they started to sit down, his eyes searching for an opening in the crowd at the bar. It smelled as if someone had got sick. He knew instinctively that everything was over now. He had committed the one unforgivable sin—*he had obligated them to him*. Bitterly he thought of the ancient and cynical Arab curse, "May you save the Sultan's life." The Sultan usually killed the man who saved his life, for he couldn't bear the obligation. Alex knew he had made them feel professionally foolish. The ugly fact that he had saved their lives only made things worse. He saw an empty space at the bar. What was it like to get roaring drunk? Maybe that's why everyone did it, so they didn't feel the way he did.

"Hey, you American chicken." The voice behind him was hard and unfriendly. Alex stiffened. It was the Englishman. Alex could feel the fury in his voice, easy to understand. The three toughest of the Spahis' tough, saved by their jeep driver. Why wouldn't they be humiliated, expect him to crow over them to the riffraff waiting open-mouthed to hear the story? The least he could expect was the same terrible public beating they had given the Russian who had called the Turk "Pig."

If he could only make them understand how much he wanted them to like him, desperately needed their friendship to keep from going mad in this place. But it was too late.

"Hey, Chicken, not quite so fast." Alex heard a quick step behind him and suddenly he felt the deadly silence of the room. All at once he had had enough. Who in the hell did they think they were? They might kill him, but he would show them how much guts an American could have. Chicken! He clenched his fists and whirled around. It was the Englishman. His voice was harsh and unfriendly and he was grasping a chair by one of its front legs.

Alex took a step back and closed his mouth like a trap. This was it. But something seemed to go wrong. He saw the smile on the Englishman's face, and the smiles of the other two.

"Hey, Chicken, come and sit down. We haven't got a quorum." The Englishman turned around. "Waiter, another pernod." He put the chair down next to his. "Here, sit next to Adolf." Alex felt a heavy hand fall on his shoulder. The Turk was handing him *his* pernod. "And waiter," it was the rasping voice of Adolf, "from now on, four chairs at this table, always."

Chicken had to blink his eyes rapidly to keep them presentable. He lifted his glass to the Turk. "Thanks, Pig," he said gruffly.

THE MOST FAMOUS TURK

♠

The Turkish race has produced some of the greatest generals and rulers of all history. Alladein Kaikobad, the Seljuk emperor mentioned in Omar Khayyam, Genghis Khan, Tamerlane, Bayazid the Conqueror, Suleiman the Magnificent and, of course, the immortal Mustafa Kemal Ataturk.

In everyday conversation with the Turkish man on the street, or in the coffee houses where they gossip over their backgammon games and bargain and have fun over their raqui, there is one name which stands out above all the rest. It is that of the famous sage, Nazrettin Hoja, who was the leading citizen of the great Turkish City of Konya in the fourteenth century.

Sometimes a man becomes so famous for his wisdom or his humor that his name becomes a magnet to which all clever stories are attracted, whether he had anything to do with them or not. Will Rogers almost attained this status in the United States and others in other countries have been similarly famous, but in no country at any time has one man so completely dominated the humor of a country as his Nazrettin Hoja in Turkey. Now, 700 years after his death, he is probably more famous in Turkey than he was during his lifetime. Like a chain reaction in time, a good percentage of all the humorous proverbs and stories in the Turkish language are attributed somewhere in Turkey to the famous sage of Konya.

It is difficult to analyze the reasons for Nazrettin Hoja's fame. He was undoubtedly a man of great inner wisdom who had the gift of putting things very concisely and humorously in much the same way that Abraham Lincoln did. He seems to have had a certain amount of larceny in his soul. He liked to play tricks on people, but his tricks and frauds were usually of the friendly type in which the humor outweighed the pain.

It was said that the great Turkish Sultan Yilderim Bayazid (The Thunderer), one of the greatest generals of all time, a dope-addict who scared people half to death by staring at them with his one good eye, was once marching through central Anatolia with his Janizary Corps. Coming to the outskirts of Konya he saw Nazrettin Hoja sitting at ease in front of his little restaurant.

The formidable Sultan dismounted, went into the restaurant, and ordered some scrambled eggs. He finished them off and asked the price. Nazrettin Hoja brazenly charged him six gold pieces. The Thunderer balefully fixed his one good eye on Nazrettin Hoja. The Janizaries grinned with anticipation. It was always good sport when the Sultan got mad and had someone impaled or strangled to while away the time.

"I had no idea," the Sultan said in an ominous voice, "that eggs were so scarce in Anatolia." Nazrettin Hoja bowed respectfully from the waist in the Oriental manner. "It is not eggs that are scarce, Your Majesty, it is Sultans that are scarce."

There was a moment of breathless silence. The deaf-mutes, with their bow strings at the ready, moved expectantly forward. And then, suddenly, the Sultan shouted with laughter. "While I am Sultan they had better be scarce," he roared and ordered his purse Janizary to give Nazrettin Hoja the six gold pieces. Everywhere one goes now in Turkey this phrase continuously comes up. If a tourist complains about being overcharged in the bazaar, or in a hotel, or in a taxi, the invariable answer, always given with a friendly Turkish smile, is, "Sultans are scarce." It is a compliment most people find hard to resist.

A short while later, the mighty Sultan was defeated at the Battle of Ankara, considered by many historians to have been the most important single battle in world history. If Bayazid had defeated Tamerlane he would have had little trouble conquering Europe after that and turning it into a Turkish peninsula.

In this mighty battle of Turk against Turk, Tamerlane maneuvered himself between Bayazid's army and its water supply, and then by clever propaganda methods persuaded a good part of Bayazid's army to defect to their "Turkish cousins" and Bayazid was defeated.

In a dramatic scene after the battle, Bayazid was brought before the "Limper," as Tamerlane was called because of a serious battle wound he had received. As Bayazid was dragged into the room, Tamerlane burst out laughing. Bayazid glared at him. "Allah will not look kindly on one who mocks a victim of misfortune like myself."

"I am not laughing at you," said Tamerlane, "but at the humor of Allah who has seen fit to divide his great world between a man who is blind in one eye and a man who is lame in one foot."

Tamerlane, one of the cruelest rulers who ever lived, was an absolute master of fraud and deceit. It was his custom to murder the whole population of any city that resisted him and build a huge pyramid with the skulls of its inhabitants. The British Museum has a section of the concrete wall of the Middle Eastern city of Philadelphia, which was constructed by Tamerlane out of human bones.

As Tamerlane marched across Turkey toward Byzantium, an army of Armenian cavalrymen kept cutting his communications. He finally bottled them up in the City of Sivas, in Northern Turkey. Knowing that a siege would delay him many months in his conquest, he made them a generous offer. "If you throw down your arms and surrender, I will pledge my word to shed not one drop of human blood."

The Armenians, knowing he would get them sooner or later, eagerly accepted this startlingly generous offer. They threw down their arms and emerged from the walls of the city. Tamerlane kept his word by ordering his soldiers to bury them alive in the moat of their city, "without shedding one drop of human blood."

A master of deceit, Tamerlane was always deathly afraid that the newly-invented cannon would be used against him on the battlefield. To guard against such a catastrophe, he announced to the world that he had invented a weapon so frightful that with it he could instantly kill all the members of any enemy army. The weapon was contained in four huge iron chests—each on the back of a war elephant. Before every battle Tamerlane ordered the elephants to be paraded before the enemy's lines. A herald would then announce that any use of gunpowder or cannon would result in the immediate destruction of the enemy with his frightful new weapon.

Tamerlane would never tell even his own officers what his terrible weapon was. After his death they tremblingly pried open the iron chests. They contained— nothing at all.

When Tamerlane and his army reached Konya he demanded to see Konya's most famous citizen and

Nazrettin Hoja was brought before him. The sadistic Tartar was absolutely bewitched by Nazrettin Hoja's humor but he was almost equally annoyed by the Hoja's lack of respect. The sage had many extremely narrow escapes.

Every soldier in Tamerlane's Tatar army had to shoot 75 arrows each day to be sure that he maintained his skill. One day when Tamerlane and the Hoja were watching the archery practice together, Nazrettin Hoja let his sense of humor run away with him. "Even I can shoot better than those fellows," he said jovially. Instantly he realized his mistake, but it was too late. One thing that Tamerlane was thoroughly no-nonsense about was anything involving his army.

Nazrettin Hoja shuddered as the cold grey eyes that had seen the murder of thousands of human beings turned and stared at him. Tamerlane limped over to the nearest soldier and snatched a bow and a quiver of arrows out of his hand. He thrust them at Nazrettin Hoja. "There is the target," he said pointing at a shield some hundred paces away. "If you do not prove what you said about your shooting, I am going to have you skinned alive right where you stand."

The Hoja, who was a mediocre shot, tremblingly took the bow and the quiver of arrows. "I am not used to this kind of bow," he said. He put on the ivory thumb ring, nocked the arrow to the silk string of the bow, and stepped up to the mark. He aimed carefully and let an arrow fly. To his horror it missed its mark by twenty feet. There was a roar of laughter from the soldiers and the Lord High Executioner got out his skinning knife and started to sharpen it.

The Hoja, perspiring freely, turned to Tamerlane. "That," he said, "is the way one of your ordinary Tatar soldiers shoots." He nocked another arrow to his bow and that one came much nearer. "That," he said, "is the way

your Ming Bashe, your captain of a thousand, shoots."
Allah, he prayed under his breath, let one finally hit.

He missed with another arrow, bowed to the conqueror and said, "That is the way one of your One Horse Tail Pashas shoots."

He missed again, and now, almost dead with fear, he said, "That is the way one of your Two Horse Tail Pashas shoots."

Finally, his tenth arrow slammed right into the middle of the target. He turned with a smile. "That is the way Tamerlane the Conqueror shoots, and," he could not resist adding, "Nazrettin Hoja."

There was a roar of laughter from the soldiers and finally even the stern face of the Conqueror broke into a thin smile. Again Nazrettin Hoja had saved his skin.

A few days later Tamerlane put an enormous tax on the Hoja's home city of Konya. The sum was so vast that it would have bankrupted every merchant in what, at that time, was one of the wealthiest cities in the world.

Nazrettin Hoja decided to risk his life again and pleaded with the Conqueror to remove the tax. Tamerlane looked at him in astonishment. "I conquered your city with the edge of my sword," he said; "the whole city belongs to me but all I am taking is this tax. I am being very generous." There was a glint of humor in the terrible eyes. "What will you give me, Hoja, if I take off the tax?"

Nazrettin Hoja sat thinking. Finally he looked up. "If you take off the tax," he said, "I will teach a donkey how to talk, and you will have the only talking donkey on earth."

"How long will it take you to do that?"

"Exactly one year."

The Tatar conqueror smiled at Nazrettin Hoja and the Turk shuddered. "I will accept your offer, Hoja. In exactly one year I will be back in Konya with my army. If the donkey does not talk I will immediately collect the tax—and you, Hoja," he said, "will be skinned alive."

After the Conqueror left, the grateful merchants and princes of the town gathered around the Hoja and thanked him effusively for saving them. "But," they said, genuinely worried about their favorite citizen, "how are you ever going to teach a donkey to talk? How can you keep yourself from being skinned alive when 'The Limper' returns?"

Nazrettin Hoja shrugged his shoulders. "In a year," he said, "anything can happen. I can die, Tamerlane can die, or the donkey can die."

A few months later the Conqueror's favorite son, Pir Muhammed, died of the wounds he had received in the Battle of Ankara. The Turks and the Byzantines, horrified at the horrible cruelties of Tamerlane, for once got together as allies. They took not only every ship and boat but all materials from which ships could be made away from the Asiatic shore of the Bosphorus to prevent Tamerlane from crossing into Europe.

The grieving Tatar Conqueror, unable to get the death of Pir Muhammed out of his mind, and blocked by the Bosphorus, was faced with the prospect of having to march his Tatar army almost two thousand miles around the Black Sea to get into Europe. Discouraged, he turned back and returned to his home in the Asiatic Steppes. Europe was saved and so was the Byzantine Empire. And so, again, was the only man who had ever out-smarted him, Nazrettin Hoja, who did not have to produce his talking donkey.

The old trickster did not win all the time, though. One day Nazrettin Hoja's son came in to see him. "Father," he said, "I sincerely love Leyla and I beseech you to speak to her father and arrange a marriage between us."

The Hoja, feeling that the marriage was unsuitable

but fearing that any argument on his part would be instantly rejected by his love-smitten son, put his arm around his shoulders. "My son," he said, "you are old enough to know about the frailties of the world. I would love to have you marry Leyla, but it is impossible. Years ago when I was younger, I had quite a way with the women; I regret to tell you, my son, that Leyla's mother was one of them. You obviously cannot marry your own half sister."

The horrified son immediately agreed, but a month later he was back to see his father again. "I am now in love with Handan," he said. "This time I beseech you, father, to get her for me as a wife."

Feeling that Handan, too, was an unsuitable match, the Hoja looked very embarrassed. "My son," he said, "you have exactly the same situation here that you had in regard to Leyla. Handan's mother was one of the loves of my life and again, of course, you cannot possibly marry your own half sister."

The son, appalled, went his way. A month later he was talking to his own mother. "Mother," he said, "I am in love with Melahat and I want her for a wife but every time I want a girl Father tells me that she is his daughter. What can I do if he says the same thing about Melahat?"

The mother nodded sympathetically. "If he says that," she said, "do not worry about it at all. I was young once, too," she said, "and Nazrettin Hoja is not your father."

THE CON MAN WHO WAS A KING

♠

The most extravagant ruler in all history was, without much doubt, His Majesty King Farouk, the late ruler of Egypt. Although an accurate estimate is impossible, it is safe to say that in a period of less than twenty years King Farouk succeeded in squandering at least six hundred million dollars on his own personal pleasures. This sum reduces Catherine the Great of Russia, the Emperor Nero, and even Louis XIV of France to the position of minor spendthrifts.

Farouk's only true competitor is probably the famous Count Esterhazy, who squandered his vast fortune, the greatest in Europe, on the principle that it should be squandered just to be squandered rather than for his own pleasure. His action in having a famous painting by Titian cut up into a lining for his overcoat is something even King Farouk would never have thought of. Farouk's pleasure was not in spending money. It was in enjoying the things the spending was for.

As a result of his extravagances, King Farouk constantly needed more and more money for more and more

234

pleasures. He committed a constant and increasing succession of both petty and major fraudulent acts in an attempt to maintain his dwindling fortune.

It was King Farouk's custom, for example, to entertain his lady friends at the various night clubs and bars of his capital city of Cairo and then leave without paying the bill, on the theory that his very presence brought a prestige to the establishment worth more than his indebtedness. He finally ordered all the best establishments in the city to maintain constantly their most desirable table free seven days and nights a week in the event he might possibly wish to come in and use it. The expense to the various restaurateurs of having unused deadhead tables all over crowded wartime Cairo 365 days a year must have aggregated tens of thousands of dollars. No one complained, though. In the first place, there was no one to complain to, and in the second place, His Majesty had the police power to close them up if they did not like his petty graft.

One day, to the horror of the other night club operators, King Farouk decided to open a sumptuous night club of his own and, by his own patronage, make it the leading night spot of Cairo. He opened the sumptuous Auberge des Pyramides on the Mena Road, appeared there practically every night with his different girl friends, and very swiftly made it the outstanding night spot of his capital.

People who wanted to see the King for various reasons knew they could usually find him at the Auberge des Pyramides. If they wanted to approach him on some really important matter they would often bring in a beautiful girl as bait. If she was lovely enough the King would usually, to the great annoyance of his own "date," send his equerry, Atif Bey, to invite the beautiful newcomer over to his table. Often the most important business of the realm would be transacted as an adjunct to the King's getting to "know" the beautiful new girl. This was a particularly sure thing if there was money in the business somewhere for His Majesty.

King Farouk was infamous for his trick of admiring an object which belonged to someone else to the point where it finally became acutely embarrassing to the person not to give it to the King as a present, as required by Middle Eastern etiquette. The same etiquette, of course, held that for this very reason it was grossly improper to over-admire something, but the King paid no heed to this.

An Alexandria businessman, Harold Ada, was once, after the King had repeatedly interrupted their luncheon to admire his extremely valuable emerald ring, forced to offer him the ring as a present. To his horror Farouk instantly accepted it. Inasmuch as it was not only one of his most prized possessions but had a sentimental value as well, his friends later found him weeping and bemoaning a loss that he could do absolutely nothing about.

The King was often much cruder than this. On one occasion the head of the O.S.S. counterintelligence operation in Cairo gave a dinner party at the Auberge des Pyramides for the King for the express purpose of arranging an introduction between the monarch and the representative of a large American airline, whom we will call Mr. X. In accordance with Middle Eastern seating etiquette, the King, as automatic guest of honor, sat across the table from the host, who was seated in the middle of a long thin table of twenty-six people. Mr. X, as the secondary guest of honor, was seated at the host's right.

It was during the coffee period after the meal that Mr. X made his big mistake. He took out his gold cigarette lighter to light the cigarette of the lady at his right. It was a beautiful solid gold lighter of magnificent workmanship with an expensive watch positioned in its center.

The lady gasped with delight when she saw it. "How lovely," she exclaimed, "let me look at it." The man on the other side of her then wanted to look at it, and then the woman next to him. The lighter slowly progressed by stops and starts down to the end of the table. It rounded the corner and came back on the other side and finally reached King Farouk. The monarch looked at it in astonishment and snapped it once or twice. He checked the insert watch with his own timepiece.

"That," he said, "is a really lovely mechanism. And in addition," he smiled, "it always seems to light and it is accurate to the minute." The King, with a nod of thanks to Mr. X, popped the beautiful lighter into his pocket.

Mr. X was aghast. He turned to his host. "That is my wife's wedding present to me," he said. "What do I do now? I can't possibly let it go."

The host's answer was practical and to the point. "First you've got to decide," he said, "whether you want the Egyptian air rights you are after more than you want your gold cigarette lighter back. One thing is certain, you are not going to get them both, and you may well get neither. If you would like to know how everyone else does it, here is my advice. Send a letter to your company in the United States describing the whole incident and its implications in full detail. Then put the cost of an identical new lighter, or even possibly a better one, on your expense account. You will be back at least where you started. You'll have a conversation piece for the rest of your life and you may even possibly get your air rights."

Mr. X followed his host's suggestion and ended up with his air rights and a magnificent new lighter, identical with the first, which his American company delightedly financed.

King Farouk operated with brutal decision in anything involving his own interest. One day a group of Cairo businessmen bought the Empress Eugénie's beautiful marble palace and started to convert it into a sumptuous night club. Much nearer the center of town than his Auberge des Pyramides, in a much more beautiful loca-

tion, and famous as one of the most eye-catching structures in the capital city, it would, of course, have eclipsed
the King's own club.

His Majesty was easily equal to the occasion. He
ordered his civil authorities to close up the palace, one of
the most ageless and fireproof structures in Cairo, as a fire
hazard. That was the end of all future competition. Promoters found out that there was only one possible way to
start a new night club in Cairo and that was to give the
King a generous percentage of the profits as a gift.

The King brazenly manipulated the laws of Egypt to
benefit himself. Oranges formed the main source of vitamin C for the Egyptian public and the country was in
short supply of them. Scurvy was a major health problem.
The King raised oranges on his enormous estates, but a
large percentage of all the oranges consumed were imported into Egypt from Palestine.

The King wanted to raise the price of his oranges,
but he knew that they could not then compete with the
oranges imported from Palestine. He solved his problem
with swift efficiency by putting a destructive import tariff
on Palestine oranges, under the protection of which he
lifted his own prices sky high.

Public outrage and clamor about this perfectly open
procedure were ignored by the King until it got to such a
stage that he reluctantly agreed to one concession. His
customs authorities ruled that the tariff on Palestine
oranges would remain in effect each year until all of the
King's oranges were sold. Then, and only then, it would be
removed completely until the King's next crop came in.

King Farouk was often even cruder than this. When
the deposed Shah of Persia, Riza Khan Pahlavi, died in
exile in South Africa, his body, enclosed in an elaborate
casket and clothed with all of the panoply of oriental
magnificence, stopped off at Cairo on its way to Teheran
to be ceremoniously displayed in the Egyptian capital.

When the Shah's body finally arrived in Teheran, his son, the reigning monarch, found to his horror that most of the state treasures that had accompanied the body, including the Shah's jeweled sword and his medals, had completely disappeared.

To repeated inquiries from the Persian government King Farouk was politely cooperative. "The State treasures of Iran have obviously been stolen," he said. "We are doing everything in our power to apprehend the culprit."

The culprit was close at hand. After King Farouk was deposed by the Nasser government in 1952, the stolen Persian treasures were found among his own personal effects. They were ceremoniously, with polite diplomatic apologies, sent back to the Shah under an armed guard.

One of King Farouk's least endearing habits came to light one night when Minister James M. Landis, the American Economic Director to the Middle East and President Roosevelt's representative there, was leaving the Abdeen Palace after a party. When the Minister did not show up at his apartment after the party, one of his friends, fearing foul play, drove back to the palace. He found Mr. Landis sitting disconsolately on the curbstone in front of the palace. "I've lost the keys of my car," he explained, "and decided to wait here until someone missed me and came back."

At that moment King Farouk came out of the palace laughing and dangling Mr. Landis' keys. "I picked your pocket, Jim," he said jokingly, "just to show you that on top of everything else, I am the best pickpocket in my kingdom."

The King then proceeded to tell the two startled men that some years before he had actually got a criminal out of his Cairo jail to teach him the art of picking pockets. He practiced with a suit that had little bells sewn all over it. The King continued the instruction until he could pick the criminal's pocket in accordance with the best accepted techniques without ringing any of the bells.

Every time Mr. Landis went to the palace and whenever the King came to visit him, the King always succeeded in stealing his car keys and handing them back to him at the end of the evening. Mr. Landis tried switching them from pocket to pocket, to no avail. Farouk always found them. The exasperated U.S. Minister reluctantly turned down his secretary's suggestion that he carry his keys in a pocket sewed full of fish hooks.

The most frustrated man at the Cairo Conference, which was held in 1943 to crystalize top planning for World War II, was King Farouk. President Roosevelt, Prime Minister Churchill, Generalissimo Chiang Kai-shek, and most of the other bigwigs were there, and no one paid any attention to Farouk despite the fact that he was their official host.

Finally, by dint of extraordinary efforts, he got Winston Churchill, whom he extravagantly admired, to agree to have dinner with him alone in a private dining room at Mena House. Churchill, a no-nonsense person who knew of the double game the King had been playing in the war, did not conceal his dislike for Farouk. He did not wish to leave the King under any false illusions about their dinner. Shortly after they sat down Churchill reached for his watch. He intended to lay it on the table face up and tell the King that because of important deadlines their dinner had to be a very short one.

To Churchill's astonishment his watch had disappeared from his pocket. While fumbling confusedly in his other pockets, he suddenly remembered the King's famous reputation for being a pickpocket. He glared across the table at the puzzled King. "Your Majesty," he said, "the famous watch that was given to my ancestor, the Duke of Marlborough, by Queen Anne after he won the battle of Blenheim, has completely disappeared." He stuck out his jaw belligerently. "And I would like it back as quickly as it can be arranged."

King Farouk had, of course, not taken his idol's watch but, knowing his own reputation, he was understandably confused and embarrassed. "When did you last see it?" he asked.

"A little less than an hour ago."

"Who were you with after that?"

"I was at a meeting with your hereditary Cabinet," the Prime Minister said grimly.

The King got to his feet. "Then the Pasha has it," he said flatly. "He always steals everything that isn't red hot."

The King was referring to a member of his own palace Cabinet who was a notorious kleptomaniac. He was famous all over Cairo for lifting silver ashtrays, spoons, et cetera, from houses where he was asked to dinner. "The Pasha has your watch," the King repeated, "and I will go get it from him."

Most of Churchill's truculence evaporated as he realized with embarrassment that he had shot too quickly from the hip. "I've had so much trouble, so many arguments, so much fighting at this Conference," he grumbled, "that I've gotten my belly full up with it. I just do not want any more trouble of any kind. Let us just forget the watch and eat our dinner."

King Farouk turned to the door. "I assure you, Mr. Prime Minister, that there will be no trouble at all."

Ten minutes later the King returned with Winston Churchill's watch. The Prime Minister, for once, was absolutely flabbergasted. "What did the Pasha say," he asked, "when you took it?"

The King smiled broadly. "He doesn't even know I've got it yet."

King Farouk was smart enough to know that his own days as ruler of Egypt were limited. He undertook every means to safeguard his future except the obvious one of settling down to a serious attempt to be a good ruler for his country.

When Egypt's armies marched off to the Palestine war they were outfitted with weapons and supplies that had been purchased primarily from the standpoint of how big a commission King Farouk would get on them. Egypt bought faulty planes, faulty guns, faulty shoes, and faulty ammunition, and while his soldiers died on the battle-fields, millions of dollars went into the hidden Swiss bank accounts of one of the most crooked fraud artists the world has ever produced.

It was at this time that King Farouk engineered what many of his victims feel was the most despicable fraud of his entire career. He was instrumental in persuading various charitable and patriotic organizations in Egypt to make monetary contributions to be used for the benefit of the soldiers who were fighting in the Palestine war. When the amount collected had built up to substantially over a million dollars, the King pocketed the whole amount.

Egypt, desperately short of foreign exchange and desperately needing not only war materials but agricul-tural equipment, fertilizer, chlorine for her water systems, and a multitude of other necessities, set up strong ex-change controls to make certain that her only too-scarce dollar resources would be used for necessities instead of for pleasures.

Characteristically, King Farouk used all such govern-ment control mechanisms as ways of further increasing his own fortune. Such controls always eliminated most of the competition and caused the price of imported luxuries to go up. The King saw to it that the black market in such luxuries was kept well supplied by his agents. Cham-pagne, caviar, cosmetics, nylon stockings, shotgun shells, pleasure craft, and even hashish were smuggled in over the exchange barrier and sold on the black market for the King's benefit.

Suspecting that he would soon be thrown out by his people, the King tried, whenever possible, to demand payment for such commodities in money outside Egypt. Inasmuch as a good percentage of Egypt's wealthy class was also trying to sneak assets out of the country, the secret balances illegally held outside Egypt skyrocketed to hundreds of millions of dollars while Egypt was starving for money. Much of this stolen money was, of course, hidden behind the anonymity of the Swiss banking system.

Through the agency of Egypt's King, illegal commodities were smuggled in and money and valuable Egyptian assets such as long-staple cotton were smuggled out in ever-increasing amounts. A good percentage of all the illegal transactions in the whole of Egypt returned a personal profit to the already gigantic fortune of the King. He finally succeeded in turning his whole nation into one of the greatest fraud victims of all history.

Some of the smuggling methods he used were bizarre in the extreme. Occasionally one would boil to the surface and get into the papers. For example, a good percentage of all the camels that came in on the caravans to Cairo had canisters of hashish concealed in their stomachs. There was enormous excitement when this was first discovered, until the embarrassed investigators found out it was their King who was profiting from the traffic. The traffic, of course, continued.

The United States, as well as other nations, was shaken down by the King's agents and forced to pay substantial bribes for the import licenses and foreign exchange allocations they had to have in order to do their job. The King ended up controlling the directorship of many Egyptian corporations formed just for the purpose of exploiting the sale of products that were illegally smuggled into his country.

The King's yacht, the *Mahroussa*, was, of course,

above inspection by the customs authorities, as was any ship over which the King cast the mantle of his protection. This resulted in vast smuggling enterprises' being carried on completely outside the law in which hundreds of millions of dollars' worth of commodities were smuggled back and forth against the interest of his country and to the profit of His Majesty.

At last the revolution which he had long been predicting came and King Farouk sailed grandly into exile out of the Port of Alexandria on the *Mahroussa*. He had over four hundred trunks of treasure stowed away in her hold and a good percentage of the whole national wealth of Africa's second richest nation safely hidden away in hiding places all over the world. It all boiled down to what was probably the most massive demonstration of wholesale, successful, and unpunished fraud in world history.

THE KNIFE-QUENCHING BUSINESS

♠

At the turn of the century there was a blacksmith who had a small smithy in a tiny Connecticut town. A massive giant of a man, his business in that agricultural area consisted mostly of shoeing horses and putting iron rims on buggy and wagon wheels. Israel Irons, for that was his name, had a reputation for unimpeachable honesty and was considered the best smith for many miles around. He did not make much money, but he was happy, having a wife whom he adored, and three healthy children.

One of the blacksmith's best customers was a local horse dealer named Joseph Nimrod. One day Nimrod was watching, fascinated, as the blacksmith fitted a delicate iron rim to one of his racing sulkies. "Israel," he said, "your name 'Irons' is really an apt one. I've never seen anyone who had the way with iron and steel that you have. You practically make the metal talk. I don't see why you couldn't turn your knowledge into a fortune by making something you could sell on a merchandising basis on a large scale."

There was an undercurrent of humor in the blacksmith's deep voice. "Such as what, Joseph?"

"Such as anything the average man wanted that was
made out of steel or iron. The bigger the market, the more
money you would make. How about ordinary pocket
knives? Couldn't you bang out a knife just as easy as you
bang out one of those iron rims?"

The blacksmith stopped hammering and wiped his
brow. "Banging out a knife wouldn't be any trouble," he
admitted, "but banging isn't the half of it. What kind of
steel would I use? How would I temper it? It's a very
technical problem. I use ordinary standard stock on these
horseshoes and wagon wheels and I have learned over the
years exactly how to handle them. Knives would be a
horse of an entirely different color."

The blacksmith grinned. "I made a sheath knife once
out of a worn-out file. It looked fine and was sharp as a
razor. I've never made a knife since, though."

"Why not?"

"I gave it to Jim Smith and he was delighted until
two days later he accidentally dropped it on the concrete
floor. It broke into three pieces. Made me look like an
absolute goddamn fool. Something like that is bad for my
business."

Nimrod sat watching as the blacksmith heated up
the steel rim. He fitted it almost red hot onto the wooden
wheel and then dropped it into a circular wooden con-
tainer of water. There was a violent hissing and a dense
cloud of steam filled the little smithy. The rim, suddenly
cooled, contracted tightly around the wooden wheel.

Nimrod nodded approvingly. "That's quite a neat
trick," he said. "What if I found out what was the best
stock for making knives and made it my responsibility to
see about the tempering and quenching. Could you bang
out a few knives for me? If we could sell them around this
town, we could probably sell them anywhere. How about
making a few on a trial basis? Whatever profits are left
over after the sales expense we can split fifty-fifty."

Irons stopped hammering. "Sounds fair enough to me. I'll get started as soon as you can get me the stuff."

Nimrod located some good stock suitable for making knives and the blacksmith turned out a few samples. They were not particularly fancy knives but the workmanship was excellent. Nimrod brought in a Gladstone bag full of bottles and mixed up a quenching solution. "This is the secret process that makes us or breaks us," he laughed.

The blacksmith heated the blades and quenched them in the solution, and the knives, when they were finished and sharpened, turned out to be the sensation of the neighborhood. They were cheaper than people had been buying and at least as good. The excellence of the knives and their low price was passed around by word of mouth and the demand for them grew and grew.

A year later, Irons stopped shoeing horses and repairing buggies. All day he made different kinds of knives and all day people trooped in from a widening area to buy them.

Finally Irons got himself an assistant, and then five assistants. Five years later he was running a neat little Connecticut red-brick factory with two hundred employees and the latest in forging and grinding equipment.

Israel Irons was at his office every day and ran the Irons Manufacturing Company as its President. He was proud of the fact that Nimrod had insisted that the company bear his name. By this time the company had a sales manager, an advertising manager, and a personnel manager. It made forty-five different types of knives from the simplest to the most complicated.

Twice a year Joseph Nimrod would come into the factory and mix the tempering solution for the next six months. It was the only thing that Israel Irons ever got huffy about: the disturbing fact that Nimrod would never tell anyone what was in his quenching solution. He would

come in with two bag loads of little bottles and lock himself alone in the quenching room. At his orders there was always a quantity of certain staples on hand: salt, kerosene, wood shavings, and olive oil. He would lock himself in and spend the whole day there, grinding and mixing and stirring.

One day Israel Irons could stand it no longer. "What the hell right have you to keep that solution a secret?" he asked. "We've built this thing up together as partners. I work full-time on it every day and you get half of the profits just by working two days a year." His honest face bristled with indignation. "It just plain isn't fair."

Nimrod was polite but firm. "You shouldn't forget, Israel, that I was the one who dreamed up the whole idea. If it hadn't been for my dreaming this up, you would still be making horseshoes and wagon rims. And who needs them now? The company needed your skill in working iron, plus my skill in deciding what to do and how to do it."

Israel was not satisfied. "Yes, but you have no children and I have. What if you suddenly died? Our whole advertising and sales program is built around our special tempering process. I don't even know what we use in the tempering solution. Do you want our company to die with you?"

Nimrod looked at his old friend. "Israel, I am not going to tell you what is in the solution. That is the only thing that keeps me getting half of the profits. I haven't got anyone to leave my money to, though, and I am the godfather of your children. They are my heirs. I am going to leave a letter for you, Israel, in my safety deposit vault. If I die before you, it will tell you what the solution is."

Israel Irons grinned. "That's fair enough for me, Joseph."

For over forty years, Joseph Nimrod got half the profits of the Irons Manufacturing Company. When he

died, a letter was found in his safety deposit vault addressed to Israel Irons. It had a legend on the envelope,
"Very Personal."

Israel opened the envelope with trembling hands and
found another envelope inside the first. It also had a
legend, "Very Private. Do Not Open This Letter in Front of
Witnesses."

Israel ordered everyone out of the room and opened
the second envelope.

The precious and intricate mixture that Joseph
Nimrod had for forty years been adding to the quenching
water was just ordinary table salt.

THE NUPTIAL FRAUD OF THE
MARQUISE DE CHATELET

♠

The Marquise de Chatelet was the mistress of the famous French author Voltaire for over sixteen years. After eleven years of this relationship, Voltaire fell in love with his niece, Madame Denis, and the Marquise de Chatelet, during the course of their visit to the Court of Lorraine, fell in love with the Marquis de Saint-Lambert. She still maintained a very close but platonic relationship with Voltaire.

At forty-three, to her enormous surprise and to the horror of her lover, the Marquise de Chatelet became pregnant. The sixty-four-dollar question immediately became what to do about her husband, the Marquis, with whom she had not lived as a wife for almost twenty years.

Voltaire and the Marquis de Saint-Lambert and the Marquise de Chatelet all met at her château at Ciercy to work out some plan of action. First they considered that she should have her baby in some remote spot where her husband would never know about it. The thought of the remote spot practically killed the gregarious Marquise de Chatelet and she wanted no part of it. Also, what would

251

she do with the child if it had no father? What, for example, would she name it?

Voltaire, in an allusion to the Marquise de Chatelet's many books and writings, convulsed the plotters by suggesting that the name of the child should rightfully appear "among the miscellaneous works of the Marquise de Chatelet."

It was finally decided she would have to get her husband, the Marquis de Chatelet, to come back from his regiment at Dijon long enough to make him technically and legally the father of her child.

Knowing that the Marquis loved his regiment more than either her or their château at Ciercy, she wrote him to say that she was threatened with a lawsuit and needed very much to see him. Almost as a postscript, she added that she had certain monies that she wished to hand over to him. The Marquis, to everyone's huge relief, came to Ciercy on schedule.

When Madame de Pompadour and the rest of the gossips and wits at the French king's court at Versailles heard that the Marquise de Chatelet had sent for her husband (with whom, they well knew, she had not lived as a wife for over twenty years), there was great hilarity. The question was asked around the court like a conundrum, "For what reason does the Marquise de Chatelet all at once wish to see her husband?" The answer, "It is one of those cravings of a pregnant woman."

When the Marquis de Chatelet came to his château at Ciercy, the reception he got practically floored him. Wonderful entertainment, all of his favorite foods and games, dinner table conversation that sparkled with the witticisms of Voltaire and the Marquise de Chatelet, who were considered by everyone to be the 18th Century's most brilliant man and woman. Even the Marquis de Saint-Lambert outdid himself.

The thing that fascinated the Marquis de Chatelet

most, though, was that everyone, even the famous Voltaire, could not seem to hear enough about his military campaigns. As most people considered them a beastly bore and as his wife had never let him discuss them before, he was vastly stimulated by the attention he got, particularly from his wife, the Marquise. She appeared for the first time in over twenty years to be deeply intrigued with him. A very beautiful woman indeed, all covered with diamonds and obviously, despite the formidable presences of Voltaire and the Marquis de Saint-Lambert, interested in him alone, she insisted on sitting next to him.

As he drank more and more of his favorite wines the Marquis suddenly made the audacious decision to seduce his own wife. The Marquise de Chatelet blushed, pretending to be very indignant, but kept leading him on, attacking and retreating in turn, until, on the second night, right in the middle of dinner, she surrendered. With apologies to their guests they went upstairs together in what turned out to be the start of a three-week honeymoon.

At the end of the third week, with all of the festivities and fun still going full blast, the exhausted Marquise finally confessed to her husband that she was pregnant. Delirious with joy, the Marquis received the congratulations of Voltaire and of the Marquis de Saint-Lambert and a huge party was given in honor of the occasion.

The next day, with everything legal and neat, the honeymoon ended, the Marquis de Chatelet returned to his troops, and the Marquise de Chatelet went back to her lover.

The lovers, however, did not have long to enjoy their fraud. The Marquise died in childbirth and a few days later the child also died.

TRICK PHOTOGRAPHY

♠

An amateur photographer named John Downey of Bland-ford, England, got the help of a young girl, Lyndsey Riggs, in taking a picture he wanted for a book one of his friends was writing on photography.

Downey had his camera, mounted on a tripod, all set up at his home to photograph the tableau he and the girl were supposed to act out. The girl was to stand dressed only in her underwear and a blue nightdress. She had a gun in her hand as he lay sprawled on the floor at her feet. The gun was full of blank cartridges. She was then supposed to aim the gun at him and pull the trigger, forming her lips into the word "die." Then the camera flash would go off and she would pull the trigger again.

The photographer made the scene so macabre and realistic that the girl lost her courage and muffed her first try. Downey calmed her down and pursuaded her to try again. The second try, with the cottage full of reverberations from the blanks shot by the pistol, went off perfectly. Downey rolled over on his back in a most realistic manner, looking as if he had been killed. As a matter of

fact he actually had been killed because the cartridges in the gun were real. Downey, bent on suicide, had defrauded the young girl into innocently killing him. Obviously a man with queer sexual aberrations whose offbeat hobby was collecting pictures of girls with guns in their hands, dressed only in their underwear, he set up the fraudulent tableau not only to effectuate his suicide, but also to satisfy the queer streak in his nature. He left a letter absolving the girl of all guilt, admitting, in fact, that he had tricked her into killing him. The startled coroner recorded a verdict of suicide.

A FEW RULES FOR PROTECTING
ONESELF AGAINST CONFIDENCE MEN

♠

(1) If anyone approaches you with a financial proposition, always ask him to mail you a letter outlining the deal. If it turns out to be fraudulent, this will bring it under the Mail Fraud Act, the federal statute that jails a large percentage of the fraudulent operators of this country. In most cases, this request alone will terminate any interest the confidence man has in you as a victim. Any reluctance on his part to use the mails is a red flag flying in the wind.

If he does send you a letter, be certain that every element of the proposed deal is included in the letter and that it comes to you through the mail and is *not* delivered by hand. Be sure to keep the envelope stapled to the letter.

The postal inspectors are among the most successful of all fraud investigators and have a conviction record of over 99 per cent. If the deal turns out to be a fraud, they will probably catch the confidence man and they might even succeed in getting some of your money back.

(2) Be very suspicious of anyone who tries to hurry you about a decision to "invest" your money. The argu-

ment "opportunity knocks but once" was being used with great effect by confidence men back in the days of Rome and Greece. Whenever anyone urges you to hurry about a deal, it is another red flag flying in the wind. Slow down immediately and take a long slow look at not only the deal but also at the person who is offering it.

(3) Thoroughly check the reputation of any person you intend to have financial dealings with. Get a Dun & Bradstreet report on him, or a Bishop report, or get your commercial banker to look him up for you.

Most confidence men leave a messy trail of convictions and legal trouble a mile wide behind them. They rely on the unfortunate fact that almost all their victims are either too lazy, too ignorant, or too unintelligent to have them looked up in the records. Never make this mistake!

If a person's record vanishes into thin air a few years back, avoid him or her like the bubonic plague. He may well be a confidence man who has had to "eat" his identity in order to bury his fraudulent past with a brand new name. Don't become part of his fraudulent future. The old Arab proverb, "What has been will be," applies with double force to the confidence man (or woman). There have been a few who reformed and went straight but they are in the gross minority.

(4) Whenever you are offered a deal that is out of your field of knowledge, get an expert's opinion on the situation. The confidence man usually tries to prevent your doing this by warning you to keep everything he tells you a deep, dark secret, on the theory that others may beat you to the deal. This is still another red flag waving in the wind.

Millions of dollars were lost in the northern United States by people who bought undivided interests in pecan farms at a time when pecans were literally a drug on the market. The promoters were merely unloading their pecan farms on the ignorant Yankees.

Many of the millions of dollars wasted on phony fox farms, chinchilla farms, cemetery lots, Florida real estate, iron ore freighters that go 70 mph, etc., could have been saved if only the victims had been smart enough to check, in each case, with an expert in the field.

Millions of dollars were lost by purchasers of whisky warehouse receipts in the days just after prohibition. In many cases it was a perfectly legitimate form of financing, but the prices at which the receipts were sold were so high that the buyer could never, under any circumstances, have done anything but take a loss.

The whisky warehouse receipts did, however, have some value and this led into still another cycle of fraud. When the publicity about the fraudulent sales of whisky warehouse receipts reached its height many of the buyers went to the opposite extreme and thought they were holding something absolutely worthless. The same fraudulent operators who sold them the receipts then switched completely around and started buying them back at perhaps 10 per cent of their real value. They made a fraudulent killing on both the buy and the sell side.

(5) Always shy away from participation in any illegality. Remember the case of the Salonica money operator who helped his victims smuggle black market dinars into Yugoslavia and then turned them in to the customs officials for one-half of the victim's fine.

One of the oldest tricks in the confidence racket is to tie up the victim in so many illegalities that he cannot yell to the authorities without being arrested, himself.

(6) Never gamble with anyone you do not know. If you do you are bound to be badly hurt sooner or later. Even if you know your opponents, watch out. There is a surprising amount of crookery even in the big gambling establishments that tourists seem to have so much confidence in. Mickey MacDougall, the famous card detective,

has stated that such a large percentage of the very fancy inlaid roulette wheels used by big establishments are crooked wheels, that if an establishment wants a "straight" wheel it has to be custom-made.

Always remember, when tempted to gamble with strangers, that even James M. Landis, the Chairman of the Securities and Exchange Commission and one of the most brilliant lawyers of this century, lost five hundred dollars to some confidence men in a card game on the Congressional Limited. This was at a time when the brilliant legal technician was actually authoring much of the federal anti-fraud legislation designed to protect the U.S. public against securities racketeers and confidence men. As Chairman of the S.E.C. he did not publicize the fact that even he could be cheated if he was foolish enough to play cards with strangers.

(7) If there is anything at all unusual about a deal, stop. If you are a woman, use your woman's intuition, but always in the negative. Demand to be completely satisfied and informed about everything. If there is the slightest negative, unanswered question in the picture anywhere, do nothing until you have got to the bottom of it.

(8) Do not entrust documents, papers, titles, deeds, or other valuable papers to people you are not absolutely certain of. Keep them in your safe-deposit vault where they belong. Remember the story of the formidable old lady who lost her General Motors stock to a one-hundred percenter.

If you do have to relinquish important documents, get complete, signed receipts for them and be sure they are only entrusted to persons who have been thoroughly checked.

(9) Do not build up a lawsuit against yourself for false arrest or defamation of character, libel, or slander. Remember the automobile dealer who had a car buyer

arrested because he tried to sell the brand new car he had just bought, to a secondhand dealer. When the buyer's check cleared the next Monday morning, the resulting suit for false arrest was a shocker. Getting a victim lined up for a lawsuit is one of the most profitable new rackets.